# HOLD MY HAND

Parent Guide for the Treatment of Child
and Adolescent Anorexia Nervosa
and Atypical Anorexia Nervosa

## MARIA GANCI

Published in Australia by
LMD Publishing
Melbourne, Australia

First published in Australia 2021

National Library of Australia Cataloguing-in-Publication entry

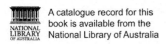 A catalogue record for this book is available from the National Library of Australia

Ganci Maria, author
HOLD MY HAND: A Parent Guide for the Treatment of Child & Adolescent Anorexia Nervosa and Atypical Anorexia Nervosa.
Julie Postance, Editor

ISBN: 978-0-6485889-4-8 (paperback)

Subjects: Eating disorders –Treatment – Anorexia Nervosa – Anorexia in Children – Patients – Family Relationships – Anorexia in Adolescence – Patients – Family Relationships.

Cover design, typesetting: Sophie White Design

Printed by Kindle Direct Publishing

This manual has been specifically written by Maria Ganci to compliment Adolescent & Parent Treatment (APT) for Anorexia & Atypical Anorexia Nervosa. Much of the information in this manual has been sourced from *Survive FBT* by Maria Ganci and also from *Unpack Your Eating Disorder* by Ganci & Atkins with legal authority to do so. Many of the pictures are courtesy of APT Therapeutic Solutions.

This book is a suitable guide for both female and male adolescents with anorexia. For ease of reading, the female gender will be used throughout the book given the higher percentage of females diagnosed with anorexia nervosa.

# ABOUT THE AUTHOR

Maria Ganci is a registered Clinical Mental Health Social Worker and Child & Adolescent Psychoanalytic Psychotherapist. Maria's interest in eating disorders commenced in 2005, and in 2007 she was one of the founding members of the Specialist Eating Disorders Program at the Royal Children's Hospital (RCH), Melbourne where the main treatment modality was family-based treatment (FBT).

Whilst at the RCH, Maria became aware of the lack of education and support for parents and developed a Parent Education & Skills-Based Group to empower parents to help their child in the recovery journey. Maria also became aware that limited support and education was offered to the adolescent to allow them to tap into their resources; therefore, turned her focus to providing greater inclusion and support for adolescents.

In 2015 Maria traveled to Michigan, USA, to train under Dr. Ann Moye who specialized in individual work with adolescents suffering from an eating disorder whilst their parents engaged in the refeeding of their child. Since that time, with the support of Dr. Ann Moye, Maria Ganci together with her colleague Dr. Linsey Atkins developed Adolescent & Parent Treatment (APT). This treatment takes an inclusive and very collaborative approach that utilizes the internal resources of both the parents and the adolescent.

Maria Ganci has continued to focus on expanding parent and adolescent involvement in treatment which has led her to recognize the necessity of including the latest neuroscience research, and in particular, Steve Porges's "Polyvagal Theory" to eating disorder treatments. This is coupled with the acknowledgment that every adolescent has different qualities and needs; therefore, treatment should accommodate these differences.

For further information visit her website **mariaganci.com**
and **apttherapeuticsolutions.com.au**

# THE JOURNEY TO RECOVERY

*Receiving a diagnosis of anorexia nervosa for an adolescent is an overwhelming and confronting situation for every parent. They are instantly overcome with terror regarding their child's physical and psychological health as well as apprehension regarding their own abilities to support and protect their child from the perils of such an insidious illness.*

*Most parents commence the recovery journey baffled as they watch their once happy and vibrant adolescent overtaken by inexplicable behaviors causing self-inflicted and profound psychological distress. Yet, despite the adolescent's visible pain and distress, their cherished child continues relentlessly along a path of self-destruction determined to achieve an unrealistic "thin ideal."*

*Most parents embark on this journey ill-equipped with minimal knowledge of the illness and the best way to support their adolescent. They are told they must renourish their adolescent who is reluctant to eat. They are asked to engage in what seems to be very strange parenting practices that contradict many of their firmly-held parenting beliefs that felt logical, comfortable, and served them well prior to their child's illness. The recovery journey is indeed difficult for most parents given that many adolescents do not want to travel the journey with their parents and will desperately try to sabotage their best-intentioned efforts to get them well.*

*This book is designed to support and empower parents as they start out on the arduous journey of restoring their child's health. It guides parents on how to manage their unwell adolescent in a loving and supportive manner whilst focusing on the tasks that need to be followed through in order to ensure recovery. It encourages parents to apply strategies that accommodate their adolescent's individuality and not adopt a "one-size fits all" approach whilst accepting that weight gain is a "non-negotiable." A main focus of this book is helping parents become aware of their own strengths and resources and discussing the most appropriate parental emotional state that contributes to successful treatment.*

*Most importantly this book highlights the important role parents play in their adolescent's recovery. It is only their courage, determination, and love for their child that provide the stamina to complete this arduous recovery journey. All parents say this journey is the most difficult journey ever undertaken.*

### *COURAGE & STRENGTH*
### *ON YOUR JOURNEY*

# CONTENTS

# INTRODUCTION

If you are reading this manual, you are probably already dealing with an adolescent who has significantly reduced their food intake, lost a significant amount of weight, and/or is highly distressed whenever they are confronted with a meal or look at themselves in the mirror. You may have also noticed concerning behaviors such as avoiding certain foods, eating alone, or withdrawing to their room and/or avoiding social events.

Most likely, your adolescent is already in treatment, but you feel lost regarding what to do and how to respond to them, and perhaps totally confused as to the best way to support your child. However, your biggest and constantly tormenting fear is probably, "Will my child ever recover?" The answer is "YES," but it will take an enormous amount of courage and commitment on your part.

Before you commence this strenuous journey with your adolescent and family, there are several important messages you need to firmly hold onto:

1. **As an adolescent, your child is in the best possible life phase to recover.** Both their body and brain are more malleable and research clearly shows that younger adolescents have a much better recovery rate.[1] We also know that early diagnosis and treatment are critical to recovery.[1] Adolescents with a duration of anorexia of less than three years have much better recovery rates; therefore, this is the most critical time for you to roll up your sleeves and do the hard yards.[1]

2. **Your adolescent needs you.** Current research tells us that adolescents are best treated within their own family and that parents are the best resource to ensure recovery. Nobody loves your child as you do; therefore, during treatment, your adolescent will require every ounce of your love, strength, and patience. Anorexia will test these attributes, but we know that your endurance will ultimately outlast the illness.

3. **You did not cause your child's anorexia.** Many parents try and look for the cause of their child's anorexia. We do not know why some adolescents fall victim to an eating disorder, however, research has identified many

risk factors which we will cover later in this book. Sometimes parents can identify a specific cause such as bullying, but many times parents cannot identify a specific cause that led to anorexia. However, it is important to identify any risk or maintaining factors so that your therapist can address these during treatment whilst you renourish your child. Regardless of any causes and/or risk factors, the bottom line is that renourishment and normalized eating are required for recovery.

4. **Let go of any feelings of shame or blame.** Many parents may feel shame and blame; however, these have no place in treatment and will only deter you from the task ahead. The best thing you can do is to learn as much as possible about your adolescent and the illness so that you are best equipped to outlast the illness. Hopefully, this book will provide you with valuable information you can put to good use.

Whilst there are many types of eating disorders, the focus of this book will be on the treatment of anorexia and atypical anorexia. Whilst both have many similar symptoms, the treatment is delivered slightly different with the aim to meet your adolescent's individual needs.

Although there is an increased prevalence of eating disorders in males, there is a higher incidence in females. As a result, female pronouns are used throughout the book. Importantly the content applies just as much to males as females and the illness is just as severe and distressing for males. Where required we have included additional comments regarding males as deemed fit. We are also aware that there is diversity in family structure; therefore, the words parent/s and carer/s are used interchangeably when referring to the primary carers for the adolescent.

Another important aspect of anorexia is that the illness often presents with other psychiatric conditions such as depression, anxiety, and obsessive-compulsive disorder, which can increase the complexity of both diagnosis and treatment. These comorbidities need to be taken into consideration during treatment and will not prevent your adolescent from making a full recovery from anorexia if addressed appropriately.

An additional factor for parents to consider is that adolescents who participate in activities such as dancing, diving, ballet and other activities that require and/or promote the "thin ideal" seem to have a higher incidence of eating disorders. This factor usually makes it more difficult for parents and adolescents to adhere to treatment. It can be very heartbreaking for parents to prioritize the adolescent's physical and developmental needs against the adolescent's goals, desires, and future career options as well as the demands from the sporting organization. Parents need to accept the importance that without a healthy body and mind, very little can be achieved and realized in the long term; therefore, adhering to treatment should be your priority.

So, let's commence the journey.

# 1

# Understanding Anorexia and the Treatment

## WHAT IS ANOREXIA?

### Anorexia Nervosa (AN)

Anorexia Nervosa is an eating disorder that affects a large number of adolescents, both male and female. Current figures estimate approximately one in 100 adolescent girls will develop anorexia and the ratio of males to females is one to ten.[2,3] The onset of anorexia is usually between fourteen and seventeen years of age for females and between seventeen and twenty-six years of age for males.[3,4]

Anorexia is a mental illness with severe medical complications resulting from severe food restriction, purging behaviors, and in some cases, binge eating. Purging behaviors are any behaviors such as vomiting, laxative use, diuretic use, or excessive exercise used to compensate for consumed calories. Binge eating is the consumption of large quantities of food in a short period of time and is usually part of an eating disorder.

These symptoms make anorexia a devastating illness with one of the highest mortality rates of any psychiatric disorder.[5] The mortality rate for Anorexia Nervosa is 5.9% and increases for each decade that an individual remains unwell.[6]

The following three criteria need to be met to be diagnosed with anorexia.[7]

1. Restriction of energy intake to the point of having a low body weight compared to what is expected for one's age, sex, developmental trajectory, and physical health.

2. There is an intense fear of gaining weight or fatness, OR a person engages in persistent behaviors that interfere with weight gain even when they are already at a low weight.

3. There is a disturbance in the way a person experiences their body weight or shape.

Anorexia means "loss of appetite." However this cannot be further from the truth as the loss of appetite is initially self-imposed and mentally driven, and symptoms escalate to the point where the adolescent has minimal ability to return to normalized eating without parental support.

For many adolescents, their journey begins with a preoccupation with "healthy eating." While this focus on health may be accepted, and even encouraged by friends and family, it quickly becomes *unhealthy* as food groups are eliminated and the number of calories ingested drops to an unsustainable level. By the time you notice, your child is eating less than what is needed to support normal adolescent development and functioning, your child is classified as malnourished. It is the low body weight and these dangerous behaviors that lead to serious medical complications.

## Atypical Anorexia Nervosa (AAN)

Atypical anorexia is a more recent diagnostic criterion and refers to adolescents who meet all the criteria for anorexia but remain within or above the normal weight range for their age and height. With atypical anorexia, there is usually a significant and dramatic weight loss over a short period of time, and this is achieved by restricting food intake and/or purging.

As adolescents with atypical anorexia do not necessarily appear underweight, there is a misconception in the community that they are not severely unwell as adolescents suffering from anorexia. This is not the case. Adolescents with atypical anorexia endure the same level of psychological suffering, and their medical complications are just as severe as adolescents diagnosed with typical anorexia.[8,9,10] What is important to understand with atypical anorexia is, that if left untreated, and your child's weight continues to decrease and cross the DSMV weight criteria, it will become typical anorexia. Atypical Anorexia can sometimes be a little harder for parents to manage because:

1.  Generally, their child has been overweight, and many parents are pleased to see their adolescent take a healthy interest in their eating habits.

2.  As your adolescent's weight reduces and they become thinner, they generally receive many favorable comments about their appearance. This usually makes them appear happier, more confident, outgoing, and enjoying their life. However, internally they are struggling with a serious eating disorder.

3.  The thought of gaining weight intensifies and fear of returning to their previous weight becomes overwhelming for them. Unfortunately, there is very little research on atypical anorexia—consequently, it can become quite confusing for parents, as well as pediatricians, to determine the correct weight the adolescent should be. The important point to remember when dealing with AAN is that your child needs to **STOP** losing weight and they **STILL** need to eat sufficient calories for healthy functioning and growth.

## Anorexia and Atypical Anorexia subtypes

Adolescents with anorexia whether it be typical or atypical fit into one of the following subtypes or groups:

### *Restricting anorexia subtype*

Adolescents with restricting subtype are highly focused on their food intake and set very strong restrictions on the amount of food and the type of food they can eat. It is common for the restricting subtype to completely cut out certain foods or food groups such as fats, carbohydrates, or processed foods. They often engage in calorie counting, skip meals, and follow rigid rules for eating, such as only eating at certain times and only eating from certain crockery. To increase the effectiveness of their food restriction they often exercise excessively either in public or secretly so nobody else can interrupt or regulate them.

### *Binge/purge anorexia subtype*

Adolescents with binge/purge subtype are also highly focused on restricting their food intake and try to increase its effectiveness by engaging in purging behaviors. This can include self-induced vomiting, the use of laxatives, and taking diuretics. They may also suffer from binge eating, which is often triggered by the severe food restrictions they place on themselves. Binge eating is when the adolescent loses control of their eating and ingests a significantly larger amount of food than what they had originally planned.

# WHY DID MY CHILD DEVELOP ANOREXIA?

Many parents continually ask, "Why did my child develop anorexia?" This is a common question because as humans we have an innate desire for meaning. There has been a large amount of research looking into the causes of anorexia, however, there is no single agreed view on why a particular adolescent will develop the illness. What the research has shown is that there is a group of risk factors that appear to have a role to play. These risk factors are thought to act in combination rather than there being a single risk factor that makes your child more vulnerable to an eating disorder.

## Risk Factor 1 – Being an adolescent

Being an adolescent is a major risk factor for developing an eating disorder. The age of onset of anorexia is usually between fourteen and seventeen years and is currently decreasing.[11] During adolescence there are massive physical, hormonal, and psychological changes as well as increased social demands, expectations, and pressures, and it is how adolescents negotiate these developmental challenges that places them at risk. For some adolescents, these pressures can feel overwhelming and make them feel totally out of control and ineffective in managing their internal emotional states and external demands. Unfortunately, during this critical period, many adolescents turn to anorexia, which offers a perceived sense of control and safety.

## Risk Factor 2 – Gender

Statistics reveal females are significantly more at risk of developing anorexia than males. The reasons for this are not well understood, but it is thought hormonal differences between males and females as well as the distinct patterns of brain development are most likely involved.[12]

Research also demonstrates there is a major difference in negative body perception between males and females. Females have significantly higher levels of negative body image, which appear to be associated with our sociocultural belief that beauty is equated with thinness. There is growing pressure in society on males to have a lean muscular body, which can make them more vulnerable to an eating disorder.[13]

## Risk Factor 3 – Genetics

The latest research suggests that genes may be a risk factor for anorexia. If there is a biological relative who has suffered from an eating disorder your child is at higher risk.[14] Similarly, if you have family members or relatives that have substance use disorders like alcoholism and/or mood disorders such as depression and anxiety, it also increases their risk of developing an eating disorder.[15,16] Many adolescents with anorexia were also very anxious children or suffered from anxiety before developing the illness. If your child already had a pre-existing anxiety or mood disorder, the symptoms may be exacerbated by anorexia, especially when confronted with food.

Despite this, it is important to understand that genes alone do not cause anorexia, however, can be turned on or off based on what is happening in their environment.

## Risk Factor 4 – Your child's personality

Research has identified specific personality traits are risk factors for developing an eating disorder, but it is unclear whether traits increase the risk of anorexia or if they define a type of person who is more vulnerable to an eating disorder.[17,18,19] There are five main personality traits that may be linked in some way to anorexia. They are *Trait Anxiety, Harm Avoidance, Obsessiveness Rigidity*, and *Perfectionism*. There may also be other personality traits linked to eating disorders such as impulsivity, asceticism, and being overly conscientious. We will speak about this in the chapter "Understanding and Managing my Adolescent."

## Risk Factor 5 – Body dissatisfaction and social environment

Concerns regarding body image dissatisfaction is one of the most significant risk factors for developing an eating disorder.[20] It is also one of the most difficult aspects of the eating disorder to treat. There are certain factors that can contribute to poor body image, but it is unclear why some adolescents develop body image dissatisfaction and others are immune.

**Social media:** Adolescents are continually exposed to social media and advertisements that bombard them with images and unrealistic expectations around their appearance. Worldwide, the thin ideal is now becoming the norm, and scores of social media influencers promote products, services, and ways of life that are often idealistic and, in some cases, fictitious. Added to this is the widespread use of social apps such as Instagram and Snapchat that allow adolescents to score the appearance of others as well as give feedback on how others rate them and their bodies.

This continual pressure encourages adolescents to be self-focused and highly critical of their physical appearance. They can become consumed with what they don't like about themselves and magnify how poorly they meet the high standards set in the media. This is a vicious cycle that is hard to escape. Adolescents are left thinking they would be happier and more popular if they could change their bodies to be more like the ideals that are continually reinforced.

**Influence of sporting activities:** For many adolescents, sports are important, and participation in sports is highly encouraged. While this can be a good thing for self-esteem and general health, there can be very unrealistic expectations placed on an adolescent's fitness level and body shape. These expectations can be made worse by the well-developed system behind these organized physical activities that seeks to set higher and higher standards of success. There are sporting staff and sporting club coaches who actively promote weight management to increase the chance of success. It is no wonder that many adolescents who participate in sports and other organized physical activities where weight has an impact on performance (dancing, gymnastics, rowing, and endurance sports such as running) have a higher incidence of eating disorders.[21]

**Societal focus on healthy eating:** This is further encouraged by Government campaigns aimed at reducing obesity and promoting healthy eating.

Healthy eating usually involves eating a wide variety of foods to provide a balance of nutrients to maintain health. However, the downside to the "healthy eating" message is that there are healthy and unhealthy foods and that one must cut out the unhealthy foods completely. Diets calling for no fat, no processed foods, no carbs, no sugar, or no dairy can be dangerous to an adolescent's health, and it is no surprise then that both dieting and food restriction are risk factors for developing a more serious eating disorder.

Adding to the pressure on adolescents is the very strong medical and health focus in Western societies on obesity which has placed a significant social stigma on being overweight. The Government, media, and schools now send a clear message to adolescents that they need to watch what they eat, exercise regularly, and make concerted efforts to avoid obesity. These campaigns are well-meaning but can lead to the restriction of food groups and other counterproductive activities.

## Risk Factor 6 – Personal life experience

Also playing a role in the likelihood of developing a serious eating disorder are stressful life events. These events may not seem important at the time, but many adolescents with anorexia report an experience or transition that has affected them and been a precursor to becoming ill. This can include major events such as moving school, being bullied either at school or on social media, personal injury, an illness of a family member, a relationship breakup, and also less obvious occurrences such as dealing with a new friendship group. Many adolescents have been exposed to negative comments about their weight and shape which has a devastating impact leaving them very sensitive to other people's perception of them or being further judged.

The key factor is the felt loss of psychological control by the changes or actions of others and this has opened the door for anorexia to give your child a sense of control.

# WHY IT IS DANGEROUS TO GET ANOREXIA DURING ADOLESCENCE?

Adolescence is a critical developmental phase that involves the transition from childhood to adulthood. This transition is biologically driven and the body's focus during this time is to lay the strongest and most efficient foundations for your child to function effectively as an adult and give them the best chance of leading a long and productive life.

During adolescence, the body undergoes many major physical changes. These changes happen very rapidly and require huge amounts of nutrients to consolidate one's growth potential. It is also the time when significant restructuring of the brain occurs such as myelination and synaptic pruning which increases the brain's speed and efficiency. The reorganization of the brain usually takes a little longer than the physical changes and does not fully consolidate until early adulthood. Because of this, many adolescents experience times of emotional turmoil and mood swings as their brain consolidates and develops. Any prolonged food restriction during adolescence interferes with growth potential and brain development and may result in negative long-term consequences that can never be fully reversed.

Many adolescents welcome the physical changes but for many others, the changes are not welcome and lead to fear and anxiety about approaching maturity. Maturity fears are quite common for many adolescents, and feeling ill-equipped to deal with all the ensuing problems and responsibilities of adulthood can cause a lot of stress for an adolescent. Throughout the developmental process, almost all adolescents will experience moments of confusion, doubt, and inadequacy while adapting to the changes in their body.

## PHYSICAL DEVELOPMENT

A primary focus of recovery from anorexia is physical recovery. Therefore, it is important that you understand how anorexia impacts your adolescent's organs and biological systems within their body.

# FIGURE 1. PHYSICAL CONSEQUENCES OF ANOREXIA

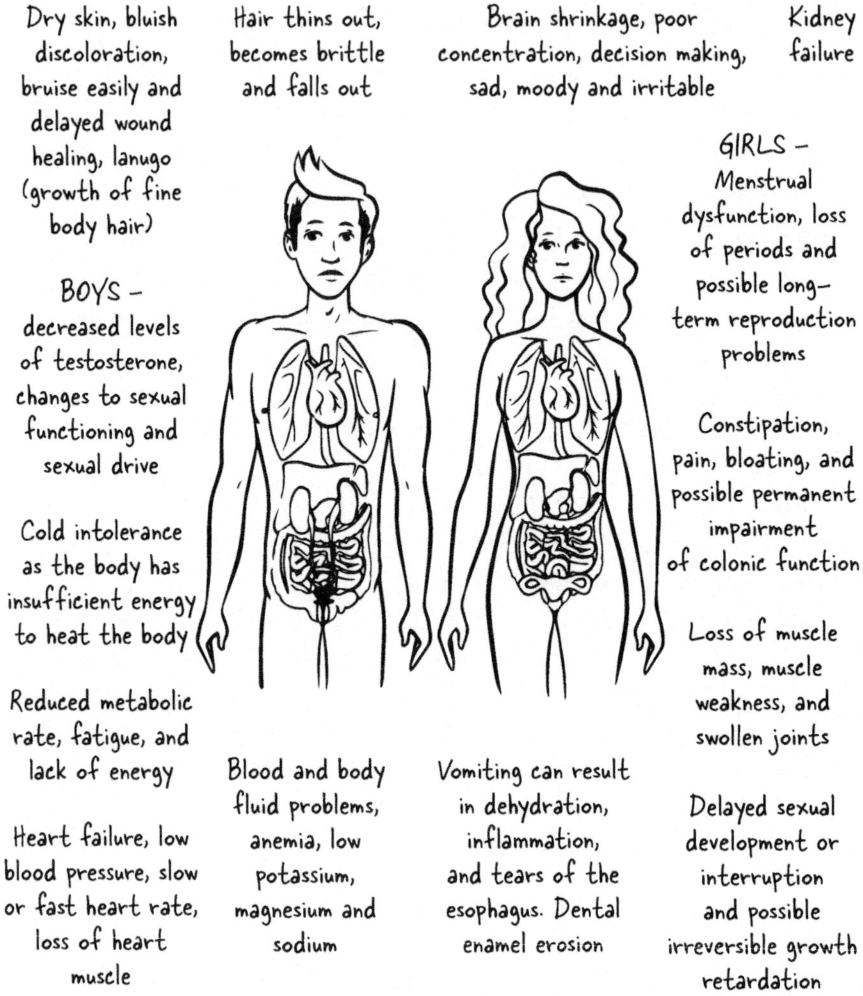

Dry skin, bluish discoloration, bruise easily and delayed wound healing, lanugo (growth of fine body hair)

Hair thins out, becomes brittle and falls out

Brain shrinkage, poor concentration, decision making, sad, moody and irritable

Kidney failure

BOYS – decreased levels of testosterone, changes to sexual functioning and sexual drive

GIRLS – Menstrual dysfunction, loss of periods and possible long–term reproduction problems

Cold intolerance as the body has insufficient energy to heat the body

Constipation, pain, bloating, and possible permanent impairment of colonic function

Reduced metabolic rate, fatigue, and lack of energy

Loss of muscle mass, muscle weakness, and swollen joints

Blood and body fluid problems, anemia, low potassium, magnesium and sodium

Vomiting can result in dehydration, inflammation, and tears of the esophagus. Dental enamel erosion

Heart failure, low blood pressure, slow or fast heart rate, loss of heart muscle

Delayed sexual development or interruption and possible irreversible growth retardation

During puberty, increased energy is required to support the rapid growth spurts that occur. Any decreases in energy during this time will interrupt these growth spurts leading to possible growth retardation or resulting in permanent short stature.

Sexual maturation is also achieved during adolescence, and any nutritional deficiencies can result in delayed sexual development, which can have a devastating impact on the female reproductive system. Impacts can include menstrual dysfunction, loss of periods, and possible long-term reproductive problems. For males, decreased levels of testosterone lead to delays in sexual maturity.

Adolescence is also a critical time for establishing peak bone density and skeletal bone growth. For bones to mature properly, intake of iron and calcium must increase as, by nineteen years of age, up to 90 percent of bone density is accumulated.[22] This is doubly important as it lays the foundation for strong, healthy bones during adulthood. Reduced intake depletes bone density leaving your child at risk for osteopenia, osteoporosis, and fractures in later life. Figure 2 provides an overview of how bone density is achieved.

## FIGURE 2. BONE DENSITY OVER TIME

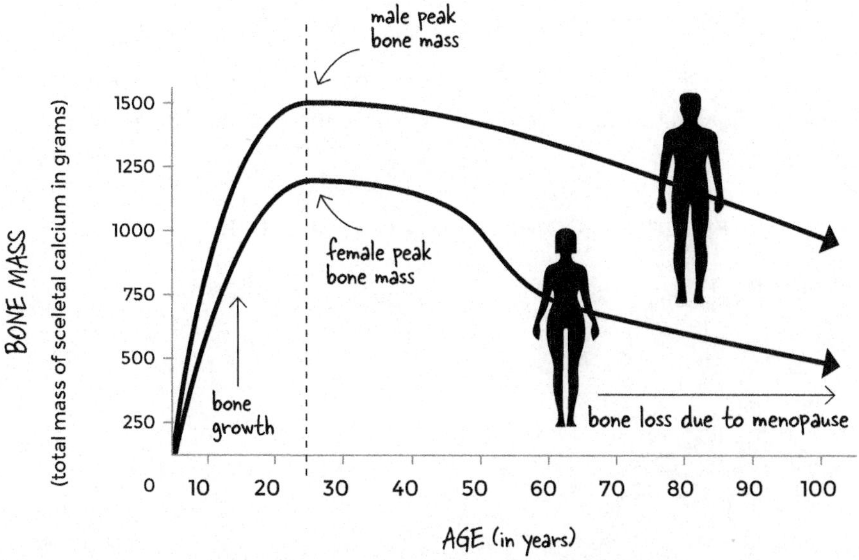

## NEURAL DEVELOPMENT

Just like the devastation on the physical body, starvation from anorexia continues its damage in the brain. This is a critical aspect of anorexia, and we refer to the brain continuously throughout this book. From birth to approximately ten years of age, the brain accumulates billions of neural connections called synapses which power the increase in the brain's capabilities as we grow. During puberty—which typically commences at around ten to twelve years of age for girls and twelve to fifteen years of age for boys—the brain begins synaptic pruning and myelination. Synaptic pruning aims to increase the efficiency of the brain and involves the removal of unused and unessential synaptic connections. Simultaneously synaptic connections that are heavily used are strengthened. This refinement of the brain is what promotes the development of greater capabilities and specialization in functions that are important and essential for your child to achieve their potential.

At the same time as synaptic pruning occurs, the brain increases myelination of the neurons. Myelin is a fatty substance that insulates the neuron's axon and dramatically increases the brain's transmission of electrical impulses between neurons as shown in Figure 3 as the wrapping on the tail of the neuron. Myelination makes neural communication quicker and more efficient by increasing transmission speeds—it is like turbocharging thinking. Therefore, we encourage you to stay on task with renourishing your adolescent during treatment.

## FIGURE 3. COMPONENTS OF A NEURON

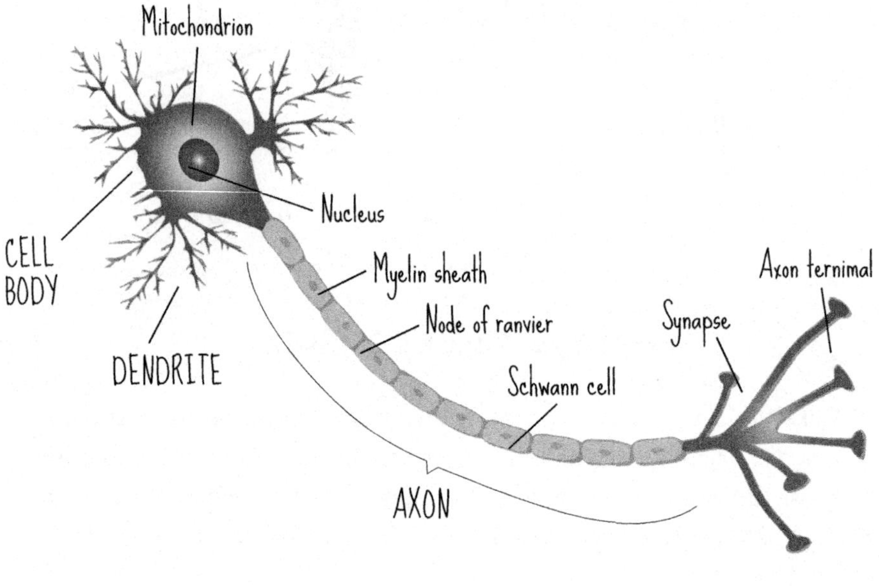

# IMPACT OF ANOREXIA
# ON YOUR FAMILY

Apart from the devastating psychological and physiological impact on your child, anorexia can have an overwhelming and distressing impact on the family. The severity of the anorexia and the intensity of the treatment can place many families under enormous stress.

At times, your adolescent's non-compliance during meals may result in many battles between you and your adolescent, and perhaps battles with your partner if you both do not agree on how to manage and respond to your adolescent. The continual conflict over food and weight gain may result in your child acting out and their extreme behavior may frighten and distress you—given that you have never witnessed your child acting this way.

An important component of the treatment, and a major task for families, is to learn to separate the illness from their child which is referred to as "externalization." The Venn diagram in Figure 4 helps parents understand that their adolescent is overcome and driven by anorexic thoughts that make them non-compliant to treatment. The stronger the anorexia the less you will see of your healthy child. Accepting this fact will help you realize that it is not your adolescent, but the anorexia that is driving their behavior. It will also help you tolerate your adolescent's anger and negative behaviors and respond in a more compassionate and blameless manner to their non-compliance and distress.

FIGURE 4. EXTERNALIZATION OF ANOREXIA

Another aspect to consider is younger siblings. They are extremely vulnerable when witnessing high levels of distress, abuse, and acting out behavior of their unwell sibling. Some siblings may feel resentful of their unwell sister or brother because they feel their parents have no time for them—given that parents must devote the majority of their time to refeeding and attending to their anorexic child.

Despite the demands on your time due to renourishing your child, it is important to try and maintain the daily routine of siblings so as to minimize any resentful feelings whilst at the same time ensuring that they are included in the treatment. Most siblings worry about the health of their unwell brother or sister so it is important that they are provided with sufficient information about the illness and treatment, and also reassured that their ill sibling will be ok.

Some siblings also worry excessively when they see their parents distressed and may worry about the impact on their parents' health. It is important to be aware of these issues, provide reassurance, and speak to your therapist if you have any concerns regarding your adolescent's siblings.

It also is important that you take care of your own wellbeing. You may need some time out yourself and ask for support from extended family and friends. Remember the stronger you are mentally the stronger you will be to fight the anorexia for your child.

# THE NON-NEGOTIABLES OF TREATMENT THAT PARENTS NEED TO CONSIDER BEFORE COMMENCING OR AGREEING TO TREATMENT

## 1. Treatment needs to be family-centered

"Family-centered" means involving the whole family to support the adolescent through treatment. Adolescents live within the context of their family; therefore, they need to be treated within that context. Treating adolescents without the inclusion and support of their carers will make recovery extremely difficult. This is because we know that the psychological strength of the anorexia (which refers to an adolescent's inability to stand up to it), together with anosognosia (which is a lack of insight into their illness), will make individual recovery extremely difficult.

Research has repeatedly demonstrated that parents are the best resource to aid recovery regardless of the age of the ill person. Parents are the ones who love their child unconditionally and are totally invested in their recovery and welfare. They are also the ones who will be required to spend the long hours providing support, understanding, encouragement, love, but most importantly, nourishment.

An additional reason to involve the whole family is that anorexia has a huge impact on every family member; therefore, involving everyone will help keep everyone informed and reduce the risk of siblings feeling excluded or resentful.

Your therapist will also provide you and your family with the necessary skills, education, and guidance to manage your adolescent's distress, anorexic behaviors, as well as helping you understand your child's specific developmental and psychological needs.

## 2. Surround yourself with an expert team

Recovery from an eating disorder is a difficult process; therefore, it is important to enlist the support of a professional team that specializes in the treatment of eating disorders. Ensure that you have all your team in place prior to commencing treatment and that everyone is on the same page regarding what needs to happen. You will be relying on your professional team for guidance; therefore, you need to be able to trust your team and feel that they are meeting your family's needs. Don't be afraid to speak up and ask questions if there is anything you feel you do not understand.

Your team should consist of:

a. A therapist trained and accredited in the treatment of eating disorders. They will ideally have a minimum of three years of experience in the field.

b. You will need a pediatrician with experience in treating eating disorders to manage all the medical aspects of anorexia and to monitor your child regularly to ensure appropriate growth, health, and medical stability. Anorexia is a psychological disorder with severe medical complications due to the ensuing starvation which can lead to long-term physical damage.

c. It is essential to engage with a dietician qualified in eating disorders. Do not be fooled by the dictum that "parents know how to feed a starving child." Parents initially struggle to know how much to feed a starving child. Parents are excellent at feeding a healthy child because healthy children usually have voracious appetites, ask for food, and normally help themselves when hungry. A starving adolescent with anorexia who continually refuses food probably needs special requirements that parents need to learn about. If your adolescent developed any other disorder involving food such as diabetes, coeliac disease, or crone's disease, etc. they would immediately be referred to a dietician for guidance on how to manage these conditions. This is also the case for parents renourishing an adolescent with anorexia. Parents are empowered when they are educated in knowing exactly what they need to do and how much they need to feed, and not just guess what they need to do.

d.  A psychiatrist can be extremely useful if your child experiences high levels of distress particularly in the early stages of treatment. If your adolescent's distress becomes overwhelming, they may require medication to reduce their distress and to also manage high anxiety, OCD, self-harm, and suicidal ideation. If you have any concerns regarding these issues and/ or your adolescent's safety, please see a psychiatrist or take them to an emergency department at your local hospital. Whilst these behaviors may frighten many parents they are common in the early stages of treatment.

## 3. Treatment should include a psychological component for your adolescent in conjunction with renourishment

It is imperative that your adolescent receives psychological support alongside parental renourishment and weight restoration. Your adolescent cannot be considered fully recovered unless they have achieved both psychological and physical recovery.

You have probably heard the common myth that severely underweight individuals cannot participate in psychological work. The truth is:

a.  If your adolescent is medically unstable, then medical stability needs to be achieved prior to any individual work.

b.  If you are feeding your adolescent sufficient calories daily, then they are able to use their brain for psychological work. It is only when the brain is starved, which means they're not eating sufficient calories to fuel the brain, that concentration and thinking become difficult. Imagine if you had not eaten for a day, you would not be able to think clearly, and your thoughts would be on food. Many parents and adolescents report that, despite being underweight with anorexia, they excel academically. It is not the 'low weight' but the lack of daily intake/calories that impacts thinking. Therefore, it is important that you feed your adolescent sufficient calories daily to support the psychological component.

c.  There is also a misperception that once your adolescent is weight restored all the psychological distress and distorted cognitions will resolve themselves. You have also probably heard that this may take 12–18 months. For some young people this may be the case, but for many others, these untreated psychologically distorted cognitions following weight restoration, can lead to relapse. We know that the brain takes time to rewire, so why not assist in the neural rewiring as early as possible during treatment to aid the process and provide psychological strategies to the adolescent.

d. Research clearly indicates that the shorter the duration of the illness and the younger the adolescent, the more positive their prognosis. Therefore, it is advisable to **_"get it right"_** at your adolescent's first presentation both physically and psychologically if possible.

e. An additional benefit of providing your adolescent with an individual component as part of their treatment is that they will learn strategies to help self-regulation, which can make your task of refeeding much easier.

## 4. Treatment should accommodate your adolescent's personality traits, temperament, and comorbidities

Your adolescent is an individual with his or her own unique personality traits. Any treatment you undertake should address and/or help your adolescent manage their personality traits, temperament, and comorbidities. Understanding the individuality of your adolescent means that the view "one size fits all" is no longer appropriate, and therefore, whilst the basic principles of refeeding will apply, treatment must be tailored for your adolescent's individual needs. The current view is moving towards "precision psychiatry" highlighting the need to tailor treatments and supplement interventions by targeting specific elements of risk and resilience in individuals with eating disorders.[23]

## 5. Make sure your adolescent completes the full treatment

Most treatments for adolescents with anorexia involve treatment phases and their evidence is based on completing all phases. The length of each treatment phase will vary with each adolescent and will depend on many factors specific to your child and family. To give your adolescent the best chance of recovery make sure you get the full dose of treatment. If your child had cancer, you would not accept a deviation from the required dose of chemotherapy. Anorexia is just as deadly; therefore, it is important that your adolescent completes all the phases of the treatment.

Do not be persuaded to terminate treatment early. If you only complete phase one or phase two, you have only completed a third or two-thirds of your treatment respectively. Don't be misled into believing that you can only complete the treatment in a set amount of prescribed sessions. The length of treatment varies between each adolescent and is dependent on the severity and length of the anorexia, your child's personality traits, comorbidity, and other medical issues. Whilst you do not want to be in treatment forever, it is important that all issues are addressed in order to ensure a full recovery. Any residual symptoms left untreated can result in relapse. The Australian Healthcare system has acknowledged the severity of the illness by allowing 40 psychological and 20 dietetic healthcare-funded sessions per calendar year. As previously stated, if your child is an adolescent, they are in the best possible position to recover; therefore, we encourage you to ensure that you *"get it right"* on your initial attempt at treatment by completing the full dosage required.

It is also important that your adolescent has achieved full weight restoration and that the psychological components of the anorexia are also resolved. If your child had any pre-existing comorbidities, it is highly likely that these will still be present post anorexia treatment and your adolescent may need further specific psychological support from another therapist.

# 2

# Renourishing my Adolescent

## WHAT MAKES IT DIFFICULT FOR MY ADOLESCENT TO EAT?

Feeding an adolescent with anorexia is usually the most difficult and exhausting task confronted by parents regardless of the treatment undertaken. The constant focus on food and incessant hours spent monitoring an adolescent to ensure they complete meals and snacks goes against every grain of normal parenting. For many parents, this challenge is further compounded when confronted with their adolescent's biological drive towards individuation and a societal/parental desire to encourage independence during this developmental phase.

Acknowledging that feeding an adolescent with anorexia **is not normal parenting and not normal feeding**, provides parents with a clear rationale for taking on the task. Refeeding should be viewed as a prescription to get your adolescent well, and as such, should be implemented exactly as you would administer a pharmacological prescription.

Feeding your adolescent requires a totally different skill set and approach during treatment. Many therapists will usually tell parents that they have the expertise to feed their adolescent and to draw from the experience of feeding their healthy child. Whilst this view can be helpful as most parents were very proficient at feeding their healthy adolescent, the landscape has now changed. Their once healthy adolescent probably had a good appetite, happily devoured all meals presented, and all the areas in the brain connected to food and appetite were working efficiently. Feeding an underweight adolescent with anorexia instantly catapults parents into unfamiliar and terrifying territory especially when confronted with complete food refusal and the accompanying distress from eating.

Parents suddenly need to calculate calories and quantities of food required to achieve the expected weight gain of 500 g to 1 kg per week. Many parents are surprised at the huge quantities of food required to achieve expected weight targets and usually spend many hours planning meals and snacks. Consequently, it is no surprise that many parents lose their confidence and begin to doubt their own capabilities.

Knowledge about the impact of undernutrition on the adolescent body is also foreign to parents as they had previously left growth and development to its natural course. Therefore, during this refeeding phase, parents may benefit from assistance from a dietician to help them manage the dietary requirements for a growing adolescent as well as expert knowledge that will support successful weight restoration. Your therapist will also guide you in an effort to empower you to get the task done quickly instead of being left to the pitfalls of trial and error.

Parents struggle to understand why it is so difficult for their adolescent to eat given that eating is such a natural instinct and such a pleasurable experience for most people. When parents develop a good understanding of what makes it is so difficult for their adolescent to eat, they are usually able to respond in a much calmer and compassionate manner. They become less frustrated and more patient, and they become more determined to get their child better as quickly as possible to free them from the tormenting distress their adolescent experiences.

We will spend a few minutes helping you understand the factors that interfere with eating and weight gain as well as help you understand your adolescent's distressing experience every minute of every day whilst suffering from anorexia. It is the following factors that interfere with your efforts to renourish your child.

### FIGURE 5. FACTORS THAT MAKE EATING DIFFICULT

# 1. Fear

## *Your adolescent is scared*

The most common underlying emotion of anorexia is FEAR. Fear is a normal unconscious survival response which activates the nervous system into either a flight or fight response—exactly the behavior you now see in your child. Fear is a response to a perceived threat and when there is a perceived threat in the environment there is a visceral sense of feeling unsafe. Your adolescent's autonomic nervous system is now on high alert and overactivated which results in difficulties self-regulating or self-soothing.

This fear of food and eating seems irrational to you but to your child, their visceral response tells them that it ***is real***. Your adolescent has an inexplicable fear of getting fat, and that any food eaten will immediately deposit huge quantities of fat on their body. They are also scared of calories, dense foods, or certain foods which are called "fear foods." They are also scared that if they eat any "fear foods," they won't be able to stop.

They are scared of scales and being weighed, and the minutest of weight gain. They are scared of what their friends will think of them if they gain weight because they have probably received so many compliments on how great they look after losing weight. Consequently, they are scared of losing their identity as anorexia has given them a new identity. Most importantly they are scared of losing control as anorexia makes them feel in control, and the list goes on and on.

This fear is so great that it consumes your child's thinking throughout most of the day. Your child continually counts calories, thinks about the horror of the next meal; how they can avoid it; and how they can expend the calories you are giving them. Imagine how hard it must be for your adolescent to eat with all this fear!

## 2. Anxiety

### *Your adolescent is anxious*

Food and the thought of gaining weight make your adolescent anxious. Current research tells us that many children with anorexia also have a comorbid mood disorder (depression) or anxiety disorder (obsessive-compulsive disorder, generalized anxiety disorder, or social phobia). Loch (2015) found that 50% of adolescents with anorexia had a mood disorder and 35% an anxiety disorder.[24]

Anxiety is very different to fear. Fear is a natural response to a visible and present threat, whereas anxiety is a response to an anticipated threat. Anxiety usually involves thinking and ruminating about all the things that could go wrong and these thoughts also activate the autonomic nervous system through a different pathway. It is usually referred to as anticipatory anxiety.

Many parents also report their child was an anxious child pre-anorexia. If your child already had pre-existing anxiety or mood disorder their symptoms will be exacerbated with anorexia—especially when confronted with food.

Your child's anxiety can become so irrational and extreme that when you put a normal plate of food in front of them, they will see a mountain of calories that they think will immediately be visible on a part of their body they usually hate or are dissatisfied with. As the anxiety increases so does their rigidity and desperate attempts to control their intake in an effort to reduce the anxiety. Your child will unconsciously think "if I can control the food, I can control my anxiety." For some children, their high levels of anxiety can lead to a panic attack.

# 3. The anorexic voice

## *Dealing with the constant internal dialogue*

A very common feature of anorexia is the constant internal dialogue. Adolescents usually describe it as a constant voice/thoughts in their head telling them not to eat; anything they eat will make them fat; they will be ugly; nobody will like them if they are fat. This anorexic voice can be relentless, tormenting, and extremely abusive.

Anorexia also tells them not to trust you and that you are an enemy that only wants to make them fat. Anorexia seduces them to believe that it is their friend and the only friend that can be trusted, the only friend that is faithful to them and has their interests at heart. Anorexia persuades them that it is so faithful *it is* them and eventually becomes their identity. Anorexia also convinces your adolescent that life cannot go on without the control and safety it bestows on them and by eating they will lose that control. Anorexia's seduction is so pervasive that your adolescent believes they are only special if they remain thin. This overidentification and overevaluation of anorexia can be intensive and the fear of letting it go can be equally as extreme.

Some adolescents do have another small voice telling them they are hurting and upsetting you, and that you really love them and want them to get better, but that voice is so small that it gets drowned out in the background noise of anorexia. Some adolescents say they are trapped in a no-win situation—if they eat to make you happy, the anorexia will chastise/punish them, and if they make the anorexia happy by not eating, you will get angry and upset with them. Whichever way your adolescent turns they simply cannot win, they are trapped!

# 4. Anorexia's rules

## *Governed by countless self-imposed rules*

Anorexia can be a tyrannical and oppressive ruler. In order to feel safe and in control, your adolescent has developed countless rules that will ensure they don't stray from their goal to remain thin and/or lose weight. These rules make little sense to parents, but to your child they are comforting because if there are rules then there are boundaries to stay within. Rules provide a sense of safety and containment to your child just as societal rules do for our community. Imagine how fearful you would be on the road without road rules. Unfortunately, the more weight that is lost, the more unwell your child becomes and the more rigid the rules become.

Rules are very similar to the anorexic thoughts but unlike the voices and thoughts that come and go, rules are fixed and must be obeyed at any expense.

- I must check calories in everything I eat.
- Never eat anything that you have not seen being made.
- Never eat anything that you have not weighed,
- Never eat more than .......... calories in a day.
- Always pick the lowest calorie option.
- Never eat fats or carbohydrates.
- Never enjoy food.
- I must exercise/purge to ensure I stay the same or lose the extra calories I have eaten.
- Being a low weight is more important than anything else in my life.
- Never eat anything after 7:00 pm.
- You must always eat less than others.
- You must never finish all your meals.
- Only by being thin will I be attractive to others.
- Only by being thin will I be perfect.
- I must weigh less than all my friends.

# 5. A starved brain

## *A starved brain cannot function effectively*

The brain is the most important organ in the body and therefore, the body makes every effort to preserve the brain. During starvation, the brain receives priority to any available glucose at the expense of other organs and bodily functions. The brain's only fuel source is glucose. When glucose levels are low the body will initially metabolize fat followed by muscle tissue (proteins) in an effort to access glucose. When starvation is severe and prolonged the body will break down neurons to access glucose for the brain, which results in loss of neurons and brain shrinkage.

Brain imaging studies in anorexic patients have shown anatomical features of brain shrinkage, loss of neuronal cell bodies, and a reduction in the density of the synaptic connections. The loss of brain matter appears to be reversible with weight gain in most cases, but not all.[25] Longer-term effects on learning, behavior, and mood are not well understood and require further research.

A starving brain functions very differently to a well-fed brain. Many of the clinical symptoms seen in anorexia are caused by changes in brain structure secondary to starvation.[25] Starvation leads to an impairment in the frontal lobes responsible for executive functioning—judgment, insight, concentration, and decision-making[26]—hence why your child will appear so unreasonable and irrational to you.

The insula is an area of the brain that appears to become very dysregulated by starvation. The insula's predominant role is to balance parts of the brain that deal with adaptation to the external environment and those responsible for internal homeostasis/stability. The insula also regulates appetite and eating. In anorexia, impairment of the insula leads to abnormalities in the regulation of appetite and eating, an exaggerated sense of fullness, distortion of body image, difficulties in the integration of thoughts and feelings, anosognosia (unawareness of being ill), and a heightened sense of disgust.[25,27]

# 6. Personality traits

## *Interfere with eating and parental refeeding*

The current literature suggests that adolescents suffering from anorexia share many similar personality traits that appear to either exacerbate or maintain their anorexic symptoms. The main personality traits are: trait anxiety, harm avoidance, obsessiveness, rigidity, and perfectionism. Whilst having these traits may place your adolescent at risk of developing anorexia, they also interfere with your child's recovery and ability to eat freely. Perfectionism generally increases your adolescent's unattainable desire to achieve an impossible weight target and perfect body image. Rigidity and high harm avoidance will get in the way of flexible and normalized eating, and thereby making them prefer strict eating routines, rules, and diminished variety. High harm avoidance will also result in increased anxiety over any weight gain or deviation from routine and a structured meal plan. We will talk more about traits in the section "Understanding and Managing my Adolescent."

# 7. Physical discomfort

## *Interfere with eating*

A very common side effect of losing weight with anorexia is gastrointestinal problems. The digestive system contains some of the largest organs in the body including the stomach, liver, and small intestine—so problems here can be significant.

These can include:

a. Bloating

b. Fullness despite not eating much

c. Abdominal pain

d. Flatulence/ increased gas production

e. Nausea

f. Constipation

g.  Shrunken stomach

h.  Reduction in hunger

i.  Reduced production of enzymes and hormones needed for digestion

j.  Drop in nutrient delivery to the small intestine.

What can make this worse are laxatives and diuretics which some adolescents use as a way of curbing their food intake or promoting weight loss.

Whether your adolescent suffers from some or all these effects, each makes the process of increasing food intake during recovery more difficult. For example, eating the appropriate amount of food can be made doubly difficult if you have a shrunken stomach and reduced digestive functioning that makes you feel overly full before you're even close to finishing the meal. Similarly, if you feel bloated or have a sore stomach, you are unlikely to want to eat more or feel hungry enough to try and eat.

The good news is that research has shown that your digestive system can fully repair its functioning as you renourish. In a recent Australian study of adolescents with anorexia, it was demonstrated that a significant improvement in gastrointestinal symptoms relating to sense of hunger, perceived fullness, and anxiety about eating can be achieved within a few weeks of treatment.[28] Similarly, other research has found an improvement in digestion, nausea, abdominal pain, and constipation during weight restoration.[29] Like most things, it can take time to adjust and be quite difficult at the start. However, eating the appropriate amount at each meal—despite the discomfort—will get easier as you progress and be worth it in the long run.

## Summary

The above factors will challenge your efforts to renourish your adolescent as well as interfere with your adolescent's ability to eat. While you may feel it is a battle with your child, it is not. It is a battle against anorexia that creates the fear, anxiety, the ineffectiveness of a starved brain, the relentless internal dialogue, and copious self-imposed rules that have possessed your child. Your adolescent **does not** have the resources to undertake this battle on their own; they are powerless against such strong internal forces. They need **YOU** to battle for them and restore their health, for, without you, they will surely be defeated either through death or become a lifelong servant to Anorexia Nervosa. The longer the illness remains, the stronger their identity with anorexia becomes, and the greater anorexia is valued.

# FOOD IS MEDICINE

Food is the only thing that will bring about your child's recovery. There are currently no medications that will help your child get better. Your adolescent may be prescribed medications to reduce their distress, but physical recovery requires food, and plenty of it.

Your child's body composition is made up of lean body mass and body fat. Lean body mass refers to the weight of the bones, internal organs, muscles, and connective tissues. Body fat refers to essential fat and adipose fat.

Your child's body needs a balance of different nutrients to restore their health. Carbohydrates, proteins, fat, vitamins and minerals are all essential nutrients for growth and optimal health.

*Carbohydrates* are necessary for the body and provide glucose for energy. Glucose is the body's preferred fuel source. Without a good supply of glucose, the body will not function effectively. The brain will ONLY use glucose and consumes approximately 30% of the body's required glucose to function. Foods that are high in carbohydrates include breads, cereals, rice, potato, pasta, milk, yogurt, and fruit. Sweets and soft drinks are also high in carbohydrates.

*Protein* is the body's building material. Protein is not normally used for energy and is only converted when the body does not ingest sufficient carbohydrates. This is an inefficient way to obtain glucose as the body needs to break down protein in order to obtain a tiny amount of glucose contained in the protein. With anorexia this is equivalent to self-cannibalization—the body eats itself to provide glucose to the brain, hence the significant weight loss and muscle tissue wasting. Foods that are high in protein include meat, fish, chicken, milk, yogurt, cheese, beans, nuts, and seeds.

*Fat*—much of the current media hype is that "fats are bad," however, the body requires fat to function effectively. Fat should make up 20–30% of total calories. Fat is essential for normal body functions. Fat helps the absorption of essential vitamins including vitamin A, D, E, and K. Foods that are high in fat include butter and margarine, oils, nuts and seeds, avocado as well as processed foods like take-away and biscuits and cakes.

The fat present in bone marrow, central nervous system, brain, major organs, intestines, and muscles are called essential fat as it is important for normal bodily functioning, as opposed to adipose fat that is accumulated fat when too much fat is consumed. Death from starvation is due to a total depletion of body fat that is used as a reserve for making glucose.

Fat is an essential requirement for a healthy body and the percentage of body fat in adolescents should be 15–20% dependent on their age and stage of development. Very low body fat can contribute to severe medical complications that involve almost every body function and includes the cardiovascular, endocrine, reproductive, skeletal, immune, gastrointestinal, renal, and central nervous systems.

Fat is required for:

- An insulator to conserve body heat. Low body fat will lead to cold intolerance and low body temperature, hence the reason why adolescents with anorexia are constantly cold.
- The brain and central nervous system have a high fat percentage. Fat is required as a myelin sheath in the nervous system. Low body fat depletes and destroys the myelin sheath resulting in slow conduction of electrical impulses used by the brain. This results in poor brain functioning, low concentration levels, confusion, and irrational thinking.
- Very low levels of body fat can lead to loss of bone density, which increases the risk of stress fractures.

# Quantity of food required

Your adolescent will need to eat three meals and three snacks per day generally averaging approximately 3,000 calories daily if they are to recover quickly. Some adolescents may need to eat more in the early stages of refeeding because their basal metabolic rate will usually increase. Basal metabolic rate is the rate at which the body uses energy while at rest to maintain vital bodily functions. When people do not eat sufficient calories for some time there is a reduction in their basal metabolic rate and this rate can increase to 120% upon refeeding.

Carbohydrates and fats will usually be your child's "fear foods" as they erroneously believe that if they eat these foods, they will get fat. Most adolescents have what they call "safe" foods, however, safe foods are usually very low in calories. Your adolescent will not fully recover until they are able to eat all food groups without fear. Consequently, it is your task to ensure your adolescent is presented with both "safe" and "fear" foods and consumes a balanced meal containing carbohydrates, proteins, and fat.

Many parents fall into the trap of trying to present gourmet dishes and foods in the belief that making food more interesting will entice their child to eat. A child suffering from anorexia will hate most foods so your well-intentioned efforts may not be appreciated. Remember you are not running a restaurant but restoring your child's health. The only important thing is to get the right quantity of food into your child to gain weight. Therefore, good, wholesome, and nutritious foods should be your main goal. Many parents find that it is easier to increase the calorie density of food (i.e., more calories) instead of the quantity, but it will be up to you to find a way to ensure your child has the required calories **every meal, every day** until their physical health is restored.

Following meals, your adolescent will complain of feeling full, sick, bloated, and having a sore tummy. This is quite normal. During starvation, the stomach shrinks a little, and now with the increased intake, the stomach will need to stretch and return to its normal size. This discomfort will not last long and a heat bag on their stomach after meals may help.

Many adolescents complain of constipation. This is also quite common and will resolve with normal eating as the digestive system returns to its normal functioning. Whilst water and juice can assist with regularity, it is important to remember that allowing your child to drink too much water will fill your child up and make it more difficult for them to eat their meals.

The adolescent years are the second most intense phase of growth beyond the 1st year of life. All adolescents require adequate calcium given that adolescence is the time when they accumulate their peak bone density. Osteoporosis is a significant risk factor for adolescents with a prolonged eating disorder. During starvation, your child may lose bone density or not accrue bone mass, so it is important to get enough calcium in the diet to help replenish it. Teenagers require 3–4 servings of dairy every day. A serving of dairy is 250 ml milk, 200 gm yogurt, 50 g of hard cheese such as cheddar or 120 g of ricotta cheese. Many other factors contribute to strong bone health such as sufficient Vitamin D, and return of menses (estrogen) for females, and sufficient testosterone in males. This should be discussed with your pediatrician, who will usually order a bone density test for your adolescent.

Having a diverse community of gut bacteria is important to health and the latest research suggests that the diversity of the gut microbiota in individuals with anorexia may be reduced possibly due to starvation.[30] Although not tested, a probiotic and/or yogurt may be useful to restore healthy gut microbes.

Your child's anorexia will also engage in many distracting "food" behaviors parents struggle to understand. Many of the behaviors are to avoid food because it is difficult for your child to eat. They are also an attempt to distract you from your task of refeeding. It is best to stop these behaviors as quickly as possible.

Examples of distracting behaviors are:

· Breaks/cuts food into small pieces

· Smearing food on plate

· Eats with a teaspoon

· Holding food in mouth and not swallowing

- Throwing away food/hiding food
- Running away from the table
- Extreme language
- Screaming or crying
- Breaking crockery/furniture
- Attempts to harm themselves with fork, knife, etc.

## Modeling

Modeling is a process of learning whereby children imitate the behavior of their parents without explicit direction, hence the term role-model.

It will be difficult for your adolescent to eat three meals and three snacks if the family does not model appropriate and normal eating behaviors such as eating regular meals, not skipping meals, eating together as a family, etc.

Many families struggle to find a time to eat a family meal together despite their best intentions to do so due to work and sporting commitments. If possible, it will usually be easier for your adolescent to eat if you can set aside regular mealtimes with all the family members present to provide support. Eating together also gives the underlying message that eating and mealtimes are important, and are also a time to be together sharing and engaging in family conversations. This is the social aspect of food which is just as important as the "fuel" aspect of food.

During mealtimes, many adolescents will complain that they are eating more than their siblings and/or their parents. Some parents, in an effort to make it easier for their adolescent, will increase their own or the siblings' food intake. This is not advisable, and it only reinforces the anorexia's desire for control. Gently tell your adolescent that they are the one that is unwell and that once recovered their intake will be reduced to the quantities of their healthy siblings.

Most adolescents will be highly anxious about what you are going to feed them, hence they will want to be involved in food shopping, planning, and cooking of the meals. Having your adolescent with you during these times will usually result in arguments. Your child will want you to buy low-calorie or diet foods and during meal preparation, your child will also become anxious and try and convince you not to add high-calorie ingredients such as oil, butter, etc. Therefore, it will be easier for you to shop, cook and plan meals without your adolescent present. Gently explain to your adolescent that you know what their body needs and what you need to do to make them better, also as they recover all choices will be returned to them.

Parents who have suffered from an eating disorder or are currently struggling with an eating disorder may find it extremely difficult to manage and supervise their adolescent at mealtimes. Such parents have reported that watching their adolescent eat the quantities of food required triggers past memories of their own eating difficulties. They also report feelings of disgust watching their adolescent eat the large amounts of food required for recovery whilst also acknowledging that their child needs to eat. If you are struggling with this difficulty, do not feel reluctant or embarrassed to raise the situation with your therapist who will help you explore ways to manage refeeding.

Given the strong emphasis in the media on health, wellbeing and weight, many families worry about their weight and shape and many families engage in weight control strategies, diets, restrained eating, health foods, and exercise, etc. It will be easier for you to manage and refeed your adolescent if engagement in any of these activities is temporarily suspended until your child recovers. Instead focus on 'normalized' eating, which is eating a variety of foods without fear and eating for pleasure and enjoyment.

# EATING OUTSIDE THE HOME ENVIRONMENT

## Eating at school

Returning to school and eating at school in front of peers will be a major step for your adolescent. Their anxiety and fear of eating are already high; therefore, the thought of eating in front of peers and others, as well as worrying what others will think of them just compounds their anxiety making it unbearable.

During the early stages of renourishment, it is recommended that meals at school be supervised by parents. This is to ensure your adolescent is consuming everything you give them, and it probably makes it easier for your adolescent to eat. Most parents will organize to eat in the car with their adolescent during the lunch hour. Some parents who are unable to supervise lunches at school will either organize a trusted extended family member or a schoolteacher to supervise their adolescent. It is not advisable to have siblings or peers supervise meals at school.

If you do organize a teacher to supervise lunch you will need to let the teacher know what you have provided for lunch either by photo or email and a better option is to deliver your adolescent's lunch directly to the teacher. Teachers do not know how much your adolescent needs to eat, and unless advised will accept that what your child brings is what you have provided. Do not place your adolescent in a situation to be tempted to throw out portions of their meal as the anorexia may tempt them to do so. Remember that whilst teachers will try their best to help you, they do not have sufficient knowledge about anorexia nor the investment in your adolescent's health that you have; therefore, they may easily become distracted with other activities and inadvertently create an opportunity for your adolescent to either hide or throw their food away.

Many adolescents will report that it is difficult to eat with peers as their peers eat very little or not at all. Unfortunately, this is very prevalent; therefore, you will need to explain to your adolescent that despite this situation you are not responsible for their peers and that you need to do the right thing concerning your adolescent.

## Eating out

As mentioned previously, many adolescents are anxious about eating out and in front of others. Going out to a restaurant is daunting for your adolescent because they are fearful of the unknown—what is on the menu; ingredients and calories contained in the food, etc. One of the best ways to overcome anxiety is by exposure to the situation/object that creates the anxiety. As your adolescent begins to gradually gain weight you will need to help your child overcome this fear. This is probably best done by preplanned small steps. Decide beforehand with your adolescent where you will go and what you will order. A small initial step is probably going out for a coffee or something small, and preferably something that your adolescent will eat comfortably. Gradually build up to a meal and challenging foods.

# TIPS THAT MANY PARENTS REPORT USEFUL WHEN REFEEDING THEIR ADOLESCENT

- It is best to include a variety of foods and fear foods right from the start of refeeding, otherwise, when you do introduce fear foods it will be like starting all over.

- Don't get caught in the trap that "healthy food" will get your child better. Anorexia is basically fear of food and, in particular, high-density foods. You will know your adolescent has recovered when they can eat everything without fear. A good sign of recovery is when they can eat everything they ate prior to anorexia.

- At mealtimes don't get into the habit of negotiating, convincing, lecturing, or using logic. It is likely to fail and it's a good tactic anorexia uses to delay and avoid valuable refeeding time. Instead, stick to direct prompting (over and over again) to eat the food you have provided as this will wear the anorexia down.

- Don't fall into the trap of giving your adolescent what you think they will eat. This is accommodating your fear. Give them what you know they need to get healthy.

- Don't get your adolescent involved in food preparation, planning, calorie counting with them, shopping, or any decisions involving food as their current focus will be on the reduction of calories and eliminating fear foods. Just put the meal in front of your adolescent and provide lots of support, love, and distraction.

- Ensure you know how much your adolescent needs to eat to gain weight and the foods that will achieve good weight gain. Whilst parents are usually very good at knowing what to feed a healthy child, it's important to learn quickly how much to feed a starving adolescent.

- Don't expect that your adolescent will be able to make decisions about what to eat as their brain is consumed with anorexic thinking plus, they will feel guilty whichever decision they make. They are in a "no-win" situation and will be relieved when someone makes the decision for them.

- Try not to talk about healthy eating but talk about normalized eating. Normalized eating is what the average healthy adolescent does—eats variety, eats regularly, is flexible, and eats with enjoyment and without fear.

- Try and stop all the anorexic behaviors at mealtimes as quickly as possible, e.g., breaking food into small pieces, eating with a teaspoon, smearing food on the plate as these behaviors strengthen the anorexia. Every time you push your adolescent past their fear boundary it will get easier for them (it's like exposure therapy).

- Be prepared for resistance and a battle with the anorexia. There will be a battle until your adolescent gets the message and believes that you are stronger than the anorexia and that you will not budge because you will not let anything happen to them. The strength of the battle will vary depending on: the strength of the anorexia, your adolescent's personality and characteristics, pre-existing mental health issues such as anxiety and OCD, and any family dynamics that arise. Whilst taking these attributes into account, the strength of your persistence and support will be reassuring to your adolescent.

- Don't allow your pet dog to sit in the kitchen with your adolescent whilst eating. Many pets have been secretly fed the meal you thought your adolescent had eaten.

- Make sure you display parental unity regarding what your child needs to eat; that the meal is to be finished; that you will not negotiate with anorexia; and that you will back each other up. If anorexia sees any weakness in either parent, it will exploit it.
- Be vigilant by sitting with and supervising your adolescent to eat the whole meal you provide. Your adolescent may hide food up sleeves, in pockets, in serviettes, and many places that will surprise you. They will do anything to avoid eating if given half the chance.
- Despite any presenting difficulties, try and make mealtimes as normal as possible by engaging in family conversations and use distractions.
- Finally, the treatment is just as confronting for your adolescent as it is for parents. Try and connect with your adolescent at every possible opportunity so they don't feel alone and understand that you love them and are supporting them by battling the illness.

## ADDITIONAL BEHAVIORS THAT IMPEDE WEIGHT GAIN

### Purging behaviors

Purging behaviors are any behaviors that aim to get rid of calories ingested. A major one is either self-induced vomiting, laxative and/or diuretic abuse. Given the distress and guilt your adolescent generally experiences following meals they may engage in purging. This is their attempt to get rid of the calories they have consumed in order to relieve themselves of the guilt for having eaten.

Purging has detrimental long-term health consequences; therefore, it is advisable to eliminate this behavior as quickly as possible. Excessive vomiting can cause damage to the esophageal lining, cause reflux, teeth enamel erosion, gastrointestinal bleeding, and electrolyte imbalance. Laxative abuse can cause electrolyte disturbances, can result in weakened pelvic floor and rectal relapse, and interfere with the absorption of nutrients. If your adolescent engages in these behaviors you will need to monitor them closely, in particular following meals. Bed rest for an hour following meals is normally recommended. However, parents' efforts alone, are insufficient to deal with this behavior. Your therapist has the skills to help your adolescent address this issue.

## Physical activity

Many adolescents engage in excessive physical activity in an attempt to expend the calories they have consumed. In the early stage of refeeding, it is advisable to suspend all exercise in order to determine how much food your adolescent requires to gain weight. Don't forget your adolescent will be driven to undertake exercise and has very little ability to stop themselves.

Apart from what is normally viewed as exercise, there are many forms of exercise your adolescent will engage in that you may not realize is physical activity. Following are examples of activities your adolescent may engage in:

- Your adolescent will prefer to stand rather than sit – standing consumes more energy than sitting – **get your adolescent to sit**.
- Restless hyperactivity – jiggling, walking the long way round to undertake tasks, excessive use of stairs, repetitive unnecessary tasks – **stop your adolescent if they engage in these behaviors**.
- Secretive exercise – these occur when your adolescent is unsupervised e.g., sit-ups in their room, star jumps/squats in the bathroom/shower – **provide extra supervision and monitoring**.

Whilst we know that physical activity is excellent for reducing anxiety, it consumes a lot of energy. Sometimes, in order to reduce your adolescent's agitation and anxiety, very light movements and breathing exercises can be very useful. As your adolescent establishes a positive weight trajectory, light yoga has been shown to have a very positive impact. However, any exercise should be supervised by parents especially if your child has become obsessive or compulsive about exercising.

## Body temperature

Heating or cooling your body requires energy. A symptom of anorexia is usually feeling cold because of a depleted energy state. Many adolescents with anorexia will try and consume calories/energy by purposefully making themselves either very cold (wearing very light clothing, leaving windows open in cold weather, etc.) or making themselves excessively hot to induce sweating (heat their room and cover themselves with a duvet/doona – sauna conditions). If you suspect any of these behaviors, you will need to ensure your adolescent maintains a normal body temperature to help conserve energy.

# HOW TO SPEAK TO YOUR ADOLESCENT DURING MEALTIMES

During mealtimes many parents struggle to know what to say to their adolescent to support and encourage them to complete their meals. Their efforts are usually received with distress and anger. Parents try countless approaches such as educate their adolescent on the physical and psychological negative impact of AN; they try and rationalize with their adolescent like they did prior to AN; they sometimes plead with them and/ or bargain about food options; and they can use threats or rewards—however, whatever approach they use they feel helpless as nothing seems to work.

It is important for parents to remember that they are not talking to a rational mind. If your adolescent's mind was rational, they would eat as they would understand the impact of anorexia. Anorexia has taken over your adolescent's mind; therefore, you are talking directly to the anorexia who doesn't want to hear or care about what you have to say. The best thing to do is talk to the horrible feelings your adolescent is experiencing by acknowledging and validating them.

Following is a formula that will assist you with this task. It is divided into three steps. **Validation**; Call to **Action**; and provide **Meaning**.

**Step 1 – Validation**: One of the ways to make your adolescent feel better when distressed is to validate their emotional state by using any of the three statements in column one – I can see; I understand; I know (their emotional state). These are connecting statements; they show your adolescent that you understand.

**Step 2 – Call to Action:** Clearly state what you want them to do. You acknowledge how they are feeling, but despite that, they need to do what you are asking them to do. You are setting the expectation of what you want them to do.

**Step 3 – Meaning:** Every person is more likely to complete an action if they are provided with an explanation or meaning why they need to complete this action. Whilst your adolescent probably doesn't want to hear what you have to say or doesn't agree with your rationale that what you are doing is best for them, it still shows that you care and have their best interests in mind, and gradually the penny will drop for your adolescent. Meaning generally leads to action.

### FIGURE 6. COMMUNICATION MODEL

| I CAN SEE THAT . . . <br> I UNDERSTAND . . . <br> I KNOW THAT . . . | AND | BECAUSE |
|---|---|---|
| This statement describes their emotional state – what you see is driving their distress | This statement should describe the action you want your adolescent to do | This statement identifies WHY we are taking the action. It should be goal–focused or connection–focused |
| VALIDATION | ACTION | MEANING |

### Statements that validates distress/emotion

- I can see that you are trying so hard to get through this meal
- I know how difficult this is for you to keep eating
- I understand this is the toughest meal of the day
- I can see this is really hard
- I know that sometimes you think I am making it harder for you
- I know that you feel really angry
- I can see how scary that meal looks to you
- I can see how upset you are.

### Action to be taken by the adolescent and parent

- and I am going to help you through this meal
- and I am going to help you push through this
- and together we can get through this
- and I need you to eat this
- and I am asking you to have a bite and trust me
- and I need you to finish your meal
- and I need you to continue eating.

### Rationale response that gives meaning

- because I want you to enjoy all the things you used to do
- because it is the only way to get you better
- because I want you to play all the sports you did
- because your friends need you and want you back
- because I love you and want you to get better.

## *What not to talk about*

- Don't talk about the food they are eating—amounts, types, etc.
- Avoid discussions around low-fat options
- Avoid lecturing, preaching, or rationalizing with them about why they need to eat
- Avoid talking about the ingredients, cooking methods, or nutritional value of the food
- Avoid discussions about feeling very full (which may encourage feelings of guilt for the person with the eating disorder)
- Avoid negotiating about food—focus on what they need
- Avoid talking about anorexia or illness—the focus is on getting healthy.

## *Take the focus off the body*

- Avoid talking about weight or commenting on weight, shape, size, or exercise—about your child, yourself, or siblings, peers, or others
- Avoid discussions about dieting or celebrities
- Avoid discussions about clothing or fashion
- Avoid discussions about exercise regarding your adolescent, siblings, or yourself, etc.

## *Focus on distraction – what to talk about during meals*

- Focus on normal day-to-day activities
- Future plans
- Family activities
- What siblings are doing
- Things that happened at school
- What friends are doing
- Movies, television, games, songs, etc.
- Play games.

# 3

# Understanding the Parental Role

## PARENTAL UNITY IS ESSENTIAL

Parental unity is probably the most important skill required to manage your adolescent with anorexia. The best chance you have of defeating the illness is by presenting a united front against the anorexia. Decisions will need to be made jointly and you will both need to provide a consistent message regarding every aspect of refeeding; your expectations of your child and their behavior; otherwise the anorexia will divide you both and ultimately defeat your efforts to get your adolescent better.

## WHY DO PARENTS STRUGGLE TO WORK TOGETHER?

Parents normally approach the parental role with very different views on parenting. This is due to their own personal experience of being parented in their family of origin and internalizing a model of their own parents. This is called the internal working model of parenting. How many of us have said, "When I am a parent, I will never do that to my children" and then one day when we are parents, we suddenly realize that we are acting and doing exactly as our own parents did.

Having different views on parenting is not usually a major problem when a family is traveling along smoothly. Most families can accommodate the different values and expectations that each parent brings from their past. Sometimes one parent will take on the "soft" role, and the other parent the "tougher" role. Children quickly adapt to each parent's style and expectations. However, when you are dealing with an adolescent with anorexia any parental disunity becomes disastrous. Anorexia quickly splits the parents by hurling abuse at the stronger parent and trying to gain sympathy or an ally from the softer parent—resulting in parental disunity. All of a sudden parenting becomes foreign, and parents begin to doubt their own parenting abilities. They are shocked that their usual parental strategies no longer appear to work. The new family crisis results in instability and leaves parents at a loss to know what and how to manage their adolescent. Parental disunity and criticism immediately show their ugly face when one parent tries to manage a situation and fails. This can result in the other parent becoming critical of

their partner's efforts because they believe they know a better way to manage the situation only to also fail. Unfortunately, when this happens the anorexia becomes the only victor.

Contributing to parental disunity is the continual exposure to your adolescent's distress. A distressed child raises parental anxiety and leaves parents feeling helpless. Despite all your best intentions, when confronted with food, your adolescent will become very distressed, will most likely scream and cry, and will inevitably tug at your heartstrings as you watch them suffer. When this happens, it is normal for parents to become distressed and overwhelmed by a sense of helplessness and confusion. Ultimately these strong emotions may convince you to reduce their food. At such times, it is important to take a step back to reflect if your response to your adolescent is driven by your own anxiety regarding their distress. You will need every ounce of courage you have to push through your own anxiety and stay on task in order to get your child better.

It is helpful for parents to accept that renourishing an adolescent with anorexia **IS NOT** normal parenting. Renourishment, for a brief period of time is a prescription to get your adolescent healthy and weight-restored; therefore, as a prescription, it needs to be administered in exactly the same way by both parents. A good way for parents to think about this statement is—if a doctor gave your child a prescription to take one antibiotic tablet every four hours, that is probably how you would both administer the medication. Both parents would adhere to the prescription and dosage. It would be ridiculous to think that one parent would change the dose to two tablets four times a day or perhaps administer the medication in an ad hoc way. If you can think of "refeeding" as a prescription that you **BOTH** must adhere to and administer as per the prescription, it makes working together much easier as individual values will not interfere with the task.

Focus on the fact that nobody is more invested in your child's health and welfare than YOU. Nobody knows your adolescent better than YOU. Therefore, this places you in the best position to help your adolescent. Your treating team may have more experience in the treatment of eating disorders, but your knowledge is equally important; therefore, it is important to work closely with your treating team to make the best possible decisions about renourishing and supporting your adolescent.

Sometimes you may feel totally overwhelmed and feel that your adolescent may be best treated in a hospital, however, research has shown that parents are the best resource, not hospitals, to get their adolescent well.

Hospitalization is not the answer for long-term recovery. The hospital's role is generally to achieve medical stability when your adolescent has become medically unstable. While a short hospital admission can achieve weight gain via various methods, you will still be confronted with the same task of renourishing your adolescent upon discharge. Some adolescents may prefer to go into hospital as they feel safer because all decisions are taken away from them. However, the risk is that your adolescent may become dependent on repeated admissions given that eating may feel less confronting and less frightening. Many adolescents may also experience that a liquid meal that is sometimes provided due to total food refusal, becomes easier than eating food. The best option for your adolescent's recovery is for their parents to develop skills to support and renourish their young person at home.

## YOUR EMOTIONAL RESPONSE TO YOUR ADOLESCENT

Let's do a quick review on the four emotional ways parents respond to their child: apathy, sympathy, empathy, and compassion. This will help you identify how you respond.

### FIGURE 7. EMOTIONAL RESPONSE

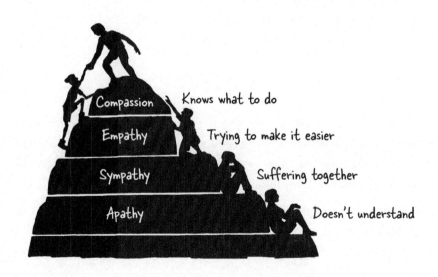

Compassion — Knows what to do

Empathy — Trying to make it easier

Sympathy — Suffering together

Apathy — Doesn't understand

## Apathy

At the bottom there is apathy. Apathy means that you are disconnected from what is happening. Parents usually respond this way very early on in the life of anorexia. At this stage, they are unfamiliar with the impact of anorexia; therefore, struggle to understand what's really going on for their adolescent. Apathy is evident when you hear parents say, *"Why don't they just eat?"* or *"How hard can it be to eat, they are just stubborn."* Responding with apathy gives your child the message "I don't understand what's happening to you." "I'm not connected to what you are feeling."

## Sympathy

Parents usually have a lot of sympathy because they love their adolescent. Seeing them struggling at meals and becoming distressed at meals usually results in too much sympathy. Sympathy actually means "suffering together." Too much sympathy won't get your child healthy. The message you give with sympathy is, *"I feel so sorry for you, and I understand how hard this is for you that I just can't make it any harder for you by challenging the anorexia, so I am not going to insist that you eat everything you need to eat. I will just sit with you and share your suffering with you."* If your only response is sympathy both you and your child will be stuck. Your child will remain in the grips of anorexia as they cannot fight it on their own.

## Empathy

Then we move to empathy. Empathy is a wonderful and important social emotion. Empathy allows us to understand cognitively and emotionally how the other feels. It is only when we are able to empathize that we have the capacity to truly connect with others.

Empathetic parents understand how difficult eating is for their adolescent. They understand the impact of the distressing AN cognitions. The adolescent also feels that their parents understand their difficulty and distress. Unfortunately, empathy becomes a problem when parents are so concerned and connected to their adolescent's distress that they become over empathetic, and it can lead to "empathic distress." Research highlights that this can occur very easily when caring for a loved one who is in extreme distress.

The definition of empathic distress is when someone overidentifies with the other's distress and actually experiences it as their own pain—resulting in no distinction between self and other. Your adolescent's distress is experienced as your own intense pain. Research has shown that when someone is experiencing empathic distress it highlights the areas in the brain that register pain; therefore, the person goes into protective mode by activating the sympathetic nervous system's flight/fight response in order to avoid the pain.

When this happens parents become disempowered as they feel they cannot change the situation. They can also become so overwhelmed that they struggle to use appropriate strategies and knowledge provided by their therapist to manage the situation due to the prefrontal lobes of the brain (where all the cognitive processes occur) going off-line. Under such circumstances, parents want to make refeeding less distressful for both their adolescent and themselves so they agree to their adolescent's demands for "light foods" or "safe foods" and smaller portions. This is a very common experience for parents, not only when dealing with a child with anorexia, but in all circumstances when carers deal with someone who is in extreme distress.

Whilst you may see some improvement in your relationship with your child with lots of empathy, both you and your child remain stuck as full recovery is felt as unachievable. Full recovery means normalized eating, and this will only occur if your child becomes comfortable eating everything, including all foods that they ate prior to the anorexia. When you are over empathetic the message you give your child is *"I understand you and will make this as easy as I can for you at the expense of full recovery."* Parents can become so empathetic that sometimes they will say, *"At least she is eating, it is better than not eating at all."* The problem with this view is that you will not free your adolescent from the grips of anorexia to reach her full potential in life.

# Compassion

Finally, there is compassion. The research literature on compassion states that it involves four major elements:[31]

1. An awareness of the suffering

2. A concern about the person suffering

3. A desire to relieve the suffering, and

4. A commitment or willingness to respond to the suffering, that is, a resolve to eliminate the distress/suffering.

When parents feel compassion, they are aware of their adolescent's pain and suffering. There is a genuine concern about their child's distress and battle with anorexia and how their child cannot relieve their own distress without parental support. They also have a desire and commitment to relieve the suffering and understand what they need to do in order to eliminate the distress.

With compassion, whilst there is a lot of empathy, there is a clear distinction that the pain and suffering belong to their adolescent and it is not their own. Their own distress is out of concern for their adolescent. This clear distinction allows parents to become very effective in eliminating the distress because they do not avoid the difficult things they need to do to achieve recovery. The message you give your adolescent is, *"I understand you, and I feel with you, but I am going to get you better. I am going to get you out of that place where you are so stuck."*

Another feature of compassion, as opposed to empathy, is that it uses the reward pathways of the brain and not the pain pathways. When parents respond with compassion, they experience a sense of doing something helpful which is rewarded by the appropriate "feel good" hormones and this increases their feelings of connection to their child and their own values.

Given the intensity of the treatment you will swing between these four emotions but ultimately if you are to get your child better you will need to be functioning for most of the time (90–95%) with compassion.

A word of caution – compassion is easy to give to someone who wants it. But remember, whilst part of your adolescent may want to recover, part of your adolescent doesn't want your help. They want to be thin and will fight to remain thin; therefore, you need to remain committed to your task in the face of your adolescent's displays of anger towards you. Be prepared that your adolescent will not give up anorexia without a fight and remember the saying: "United we stand, divided we fall." Your child needs you both to remain united in the treatment.

A good way to stay on track is to develop mantras that can be repeated internally when you feel frustrated and/or feel like giving in to your child. Following are several examples:

- My child needs me to get through this.
- We are going to get through this one meal, one day at a time.
- They are scared and can't make appropriate decisions.
- It's not my child saying that to me, it's the anorexia.
- They need to eat to get healthy. This is the only way to get my child back.
- They need us to help them. They can't fight anorexia on their own.
- Food is the only thing that will get rid of their distress.
- Their aggressive behavior is a cry for my help.
- Anorexia is tormenting them; all I have to do is feed them.

It is important to remember not to become discouraged when things go wrong, and inevitably, there are times despite your best efforts, they will. This is a time when you should strengthen your resolve and plan how you will do things differently the next time. Below is a problem-solving wheel many parents find useful and should be used frequently as it promotes support and communication between parents.

## FIGURE 8. PROBLEM-SOLVING WHEEL

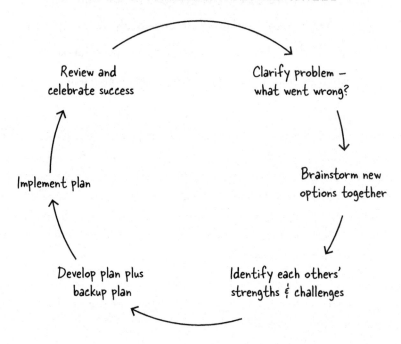

Review and celebrate success

Clarify problem – what went wrong?

Implement plan

Brainstorm new options together

Develop plan plus backup plan

Identify each others' strengths & challenges

# THE IMPORTANCE OF PARENTAL ATTUNEMENT

## What is parental attunement?

Attunement is a wonderful skill that most parents automatically execute on a daily basis. Parents learn how to attune to their children from birth. Their infant's cry is accurately distinguished between a cry of hunger or the cry for comfort? Attuned parents are aware that external behaviors continue to be an expression of their child's internal state and can usually predict what their child needs. Attunement becomes a critical skill when your adolescent has anorexia because their distress messages and non-verbal behaviors can become confusing to parents. Their distress signals are no longer consistent with their needs. Their cry is no longer a hunger signal (even though they are visibly starving) but a cry of psychological fear—fear that the food you provide will make them fat. This inconsistency creates a dilemma for parents and can make it difficult for parents to understand their adolescent's conflicting needs. Do I refeed my adolescent and attend to their physical needs given that they currently lack the insight that their body needs food, or do I address my adolescent's emotional needs and comfort my child to relieve their psychological distress? The key for parents is to do both—renourish their starving body despite their adolescent's resistance, while simultaneously providing comfort and connection to help them manage their psychological distress.

## Always promote feelings of safety and connection

One of the primary tasks of parenting is to raise children who feel secure and confident in themselves and their own abilities. This is achieved when parents provide a consistent and reliable environment where children feel safe to explore and push boundaries—knowing that their parents are available should they sometimes fail.

 Parents also need to provide appropriate boundaries regarding what **is**, and what **is not** acceptable behavior. This is called authoritative and nurturing parenting, where the child has trust and confidence in their parents' protection and availability when they take risks or make mistakes. Nothing is more frightening to a child than feeling alone when things become difficult or are unmanageable. They are swamped with overwhelming emotions that make them feel out of control. These feelings become even more psychologically frightening and intense when children see that their parents also feel anxious and out of control when things don't go to plan.

As your child approaches adolescence and gravitates towards peers, psychological safety and connection with others become imperative. As they test their newfound freedoms and start negotiating relationships and new emotional experiences it can expose them to feelings of vulnerability . . . Do my peers like me? Do I fit in? Everyone looks and does things better than me? The slightest criticism, negative comments, or comparisons can lead to feeling rejected—making them feel psychologically unsafe and drive them to anorexia that gives them the illusion of regaining control and psychological safety.

Despite their illusion and protests that they **are** in control, the anorexia is masking your adolescent's fear and lack of control over other areas in their environment. If your adolescent were in control, they would not compromise their health to the extent that they are.

Whilst the anorexia may delude your adolescent that they are in control, the illness can also make parents feel totally out of control. If parents show signs that they are intimidated, either by the anorexia or anorexic behaviors, the adolescent will feel they cannot depend on their parents and that their parents have abandoned them when they need them most. Alternatively, your display of intimidation by the anorexia can also make your adolescent feel they are alone and therefore, they are the only one that can keep themselves safe. If your adolescent cannot depend on you to make them feel safe, that only leaves the anorexia to depend on; therefore, your adolescent will continue to be ruled by their anorexia. This self-dependency and dependency on anorexia will also make your adolescent resistant to seek help from others.

You need to respond to your adolescent in a calm and non-critical manner despite your adolescent's displays of distress and possible anger towards you. You need to show your adolescent that you **are** in control of the situation and that you know what you are doing even though internally you may be feeling equally distressed and unsure of what you are doing. It's not unusual for parents to question what they are doing given that the situation they find themselves in is totally foreign. Your firm belief that you are doing the right thing will emotionally contain and make your adolescent feel safe. If parents, the people they have trusted all their life can't help them, then they automatically think that no one can and therefore, they are unsafe.

***Practical exercise that demonstrates "feeling contained"*** - Close your eyes for a moment and picture you are in a room with a group of friends and there is a fire in the next room. A firefighter comes running into your room very anxious, stressed, waving his arms screaming, and repeatedly yelling that there is a fire in the next room that is totally out of control. He states that he is unsure that his team can put out the fire. He is also unsure if they can get everyone out quickly and safely. Despite the firefighter's best intentions, his lack of confidence immediately raises your anxiety and fear that you may die and that you cannot trust him to get you out safely. The firefighter's actions have also created doubt, and you begin to question if you should listen to him and if he really knows what he is doing. This leaves you with the only option to take matters into your own hands because your survival instinct tells you that you cannot rely on the firefighter despite your limited knowledge of how you should manage the situation.

Now picture the same scenario, but this time the firefighter comes into your room very calmly stating that there is a fire in the next room and that everything is under control. The fire will be extinguished shortly, there is nothing to worry about and if you just follow his instructions and remain calm, he will get everyone out safely. This firefighter will automatically make you feel contained and safe and there is no need to take matters into your own hands because you believe that he can handle the situation.

You need to respond to your adolescent in a similar manner as the calm and confident firefighter—so your adolescent can feel contained and safe in the belief that you can and will help them. ***The message to your adolescent is that you will keep them safe and will not let anything happen to them.***

## Sometimes parents can feel out of control

Sometimes parents become frightened or equally distressed by their adolescent's displays of anger and distress, and they feel that by pushing food they are making their adolescent more distressed. This is anorexia's way to keep you distracted from what you need to do. The only chance of relieving your adolescent's distress is to get your child back to a healthy weight; therefore, you need to stay on task! Your adolescent may temporarily feel happy when you don't make them eat more, but internally they will continue to be tormented by their anorexia if they remain at an unhealthy weight or suppressed weight providing insufficient nutrition for their body to function and support their physical development.

When you are dealing with your adolescent, if you feel that you are going to lose control and get angry, make an excuse, and walk away and get your partner to take over. Getting angry with your child will only make them feel guilty. It also sends a message to the anorexia that it is wearing you down and winning; therefore, all the anorexia needs to do is to continue to frustrate you sufficiently to convince you to give up.

Many parents are also worried that by taking a firm stance regarding renourishment they will destroy their relationship with their adolescent. This is not the case even though it may appear to be at times given the displays of anger towards you. Remember your child is an adolescent and sometimes can't make appropriate decisions regarding their welfare. Regardless of whether your child has anorexia, adolescence is continually fraught with battles as the adolescent matures and seeks independence. Unfortunately, recovery from anorexia is a battle they cannot win without you; therefore, it is your responsibility to make the right decision regarding your adolescent's future health and welfare.

# 4

# Understanding and Managing my Adolescent

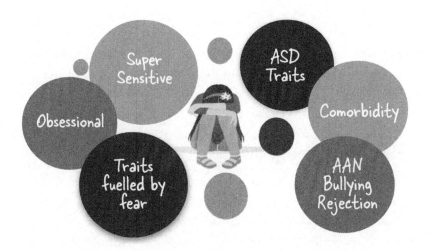

## UNDERSTAND YOUR ADOLESCENT

Before you can help your adolescent, it's important for you to understand your child's personality, temperament, their coping style, and how they function psychologically so you can manage and adapt renourishment accordingly. Every child is a unique person with individual differences; therefore, any treatment you undertake needs to accommodate their individuality while keeping in mind that renourishment is **NON-NEGOTIABLE** as your adolescent will never recover from anorexia without achieving full physical health. Nobody knows your child better than YOU, so you are in the best position to help your child.

However, whilst most parents have managed their child well up to this point, many parents are shocked how their adolescent has changed since developing anorexia. Many parents report that their once well-behaved, almost perfect and conscientious child pre anorexia has now been overtaken by "by something" that has changed them completely.

This is in fact somewhat true as the impact of starvation when merged with the physical and psychological demands of adolescence can create absolute havoc in your child's life—leaving many parents feeling out of their depth, fearful, and overwhelmed. Adolescence is a massive life transition where adolescents face new peer, social, and academic pressures that force many out of their comfort zone to begin the process of independence. Many adolescents feel ill-equipped and fearful of negotiating this major life phase which is probably indicative of why many psychological problems emerge during this period. Some adolescents develop "maturity fears" meaning that they "don't want to grow up" and want to remain in the comfort of childhood." Parents may see some regressive behaviors, and whilst parents may want to protect their child, nature is not so accommodating and continues to thrust your child forward into adulthood.

Let's start by looking at your child's temperament, personality, and individual traits as this will impact how you manage your adolescent's renourishment and distress. As you can see most of the following traits are fueled by anxiety; therefore, it's important to speak to your therapist who will provide strategies to both you and your adolescent.

## Trait anxiety

Does your child have an extremely anxious temperament sometimes referred to as high trait anxiety, or are they resilient and able to easily bounce back from distressing situations and environmental demands? Adolescents with high trait anxiety, worry excessively about most situations and often see the world as a threatening place even when there is no real threat present. This is accompanied by generally anticipating negative outcomes. Being in such continual hyper-arousal makes it very difficult for adolescents to relax, try new things, and enjoy life. Consequently, adolescents with trait anxiety need to be managed a little differently and treatment needs to accommodate and address their trait anxiety.

## High harm avoidance

Whilst everyone wants to avoid harmful situations, high harm avoidance is the tendency to avoid many situations due to fear of anticipated negative consequences. This personality trait makes adolescents overanalyze situations, be excessively cautious, overly responsible, and more reserved than their peers. In social settings, being harm avoidant can also mean increased sensitivity to negative feedback as well as being overly concerned about upsetting or making others angry. Often underpinning harm avoidance is the intolerance of uncertainty and a desperate need to know the outcome of every situation and thereby, avoiding any negative consequences.

## Obsessiveness

Overthinking is common but can be problematic when it becomes obsessive and feels overwhelming. With obsessiveness, thoughts get stuck in "repeat mode" leaving adolescents feeling stressed, anxious, or depressed. Often, the reason behind obsessive thinking is the need for certainty and control in order to reduce your anxiety about a situation. Many adolescents with anorexia become obsessive about foods, calorie counting, weight targets, and exercise.

## Rigidity

Adolescents with high levels of rigidity struggle to think flexibly and often find themselves bound by a set of strict, self-imposed rules. Although some rules can be helpful, being totally rule-bound becomes problematic and limiting. A good example is having to eat lunch or dinner at the same time each day without the ability to accommodate changes to the routine.

## Perfectionism

Having perfectionism means setting incredibly high standards that are usually much higher than required and generally unattainable. For adolescents, this can result in high levels of stress, procrastination, avoidance, and high self-criticism. Perfectionism can also paralyze your adolescent by stopping them from even starting a project for fear of failure, making a mistake, or believing that they are not good enough. With anorexia, perfectionism can become focused on the body by setting unrealistic standards regarding eating, weight, and shape in an effort to achieve an unrealistic "ideal" thinness.

## Having ASD or ASD traits

Research now informs us that approximately 35% of people with an eating disorder are on the autistic spectrum.[32] These beautiful young people see and experience the world very differently to others. Many also tend to be highly anxious, have very rigid thinking, love structure and predictability, and can struggle in social situations, hence experiencing high levels of distress. Research also suggests that carers of someone with autism and an eating disorder experience greater distress and receive less support from mental health services.[33] If your adolescent does have a formal ASD diagnosis or any ASD traits they will need to be managed differently given their higher sensitivity to their environment and need for certainty. Many new protocols have now been developed to assist suffers and carers in their treatment. A good website is **www.pearcpathways.org**.

## Adolescents who have experienced bullying, rejection and exclusion by peers

Research is confirming an association between bullying and eating disorders.[34] Has your adolescent been severely bullied about his/her weight as this factor can sometimes be traumatic to a young person; therefore, needs to be addressed. Also, a young person who has been severely bullied for being overweight will become terrified at the thought of gaining the slightest amount of weight and will avoid weight gain at the expense of physical health. Their brain tells them that if they gain weight, they will re-experience rejection. It is best to talk to your therapist about how these issues can be managed concurrently to support refeeding.

As you acknowledge that one or more of the above traits pertain to your adolescent you will also notice that most of the above traits are fueled by high levels of anxiety leading to a dysregulated emotional state. Anxiety is a bodily response via the autonomic nervous system in response to a felt sense of threat. A major part of your focus should be on reducing your adolescent's fear by increasing their sense of connection and safety. Your therapist will need to support both you and your adolescent with appropriate strategies.

# HOW DO I MANAGE MY ADOLESCENT'S DISTRESS?

All adolescents become distressed during treatment for anorexia and many parents struggle to understand and manage their adolescent's distress. Watching your child feel out of control, crying, screaming, and extremely distressed makes parents feel very vulnerable, powerless, and just as distressed as their child.

Most children suffering from anorexia will find it difficult to cope with the quantity of food they are required to eat and the consequent weight gain. Both food and weight gain usually make your child feel they are losing control. Some adolescents become so distressed that they may engage in self-harm, threats of suicide, attempts to run away, and become abusive towards their parents. You need to remember why your adolescent is so distressed and that it is the fear of weight gain, the cognitive distortions, and cruel inner anorexic voice that creates the distress (refer to the factors outlined under "what makes it difficult for my adolescent to eat").

Hopefully, as your adolescent becomes physically healthier through renourishment, together with the psychological support provided by your therapist, these behaviors should diminish. Unfortunately, for some adolescents, the anorexic thoughts may take a little longer to completely disappear. Unfortunately, for some, they may never fully disappear. Keep in mind that your adolescent has sustained a trauma to the brain; therefore, the brain needs time to recover. Example: if your child sustained a serious leg fracture it would take a considerable amount of time for your child to gain the full use of his/her leg and recommence competitive running.

## The Emotional Wave

The "Emotional Wave" was a concept developed by Nancy Zucker who eloquently describes emotions as being similar to waves. Nancy's analogy helps parents visually understand what is happening for their adolescent when they become distressed. It also helps parents to become aware of how their child's emotions escalate as they climb the "emotional wave."[35]

When your child is exposed to what they feel is an unmanageable situation, it increases their fear raising their emotional energy and activating their Autonomic Nervous System's (ANS) sympathetic circuit into the flight and fight response. The closer your child gets to the crest of their emotional wave the greater the intensity of their distress. Example: when your child is confronted with food, your child's distress (emotional energy) will start to rise. Every level on the emotional wave requires a different response.

As your child climbs up the emotional wave your child's ability to think clearly and regain emotional control decreases. When your child has reached the crest of their emotional wave they will be in a state of extreme emotional arousal and at this point, their fear and emotions are so intense that your child cannot respond to logic or reasoning. All your child wants to do is run away from the food or fight with you to take the food away. This is a natural response we have wired in us. Your child needs your help to come down from their emotional wave and return to a calmer state. Your task is to learn how to calm your child and help them to learn skills so they can come down safely from their emotional wave.

When your child is on the first level and second level of the wave, it is time to intervene with distraction and self-soothing techniques as at this point your child has some ability to concentrate and possibly self-regulate. However, once on the crest of the wave, talking and logic no longer work, and it is best to provide some physical comfort for your child such as a hug and tell them you will keep them safe. It is best to intervene before your child reaches the crest.

## FIGURE 9. THE EMOTIONAL WAVE

ON THE CREST OF THE WAVE - EXTREME EMOTIONAL AROUSAL. YOUR CHILD CANNOT RESPOND TO LOGIC OR REASONING.

MID WAVE - YOUR CHILD HAS SOME CAPACITY TO REASON AND DISTRACTION MAY HELP AT THIS STAGE.

BOTTOM OF THE WAVE - WHEN YOU START TO NOTICE EMOTIONAL ENERGY RISING INTERVENE QUICKLY AT THIS POINT WITH CALMING OR DISTRACTING TECHNIQUES.

# HOW DO I GET MY ADOLESCENT DOWN FROM THE EMOTIONAL WAVE?

Distraction is the process of thinking about something so intently that you lose focus on the original thought/situation that created the distress, sometimes called a **"thought blocker."** Distraction also temporarily takes your attention off strong emotions. Parents use distraction techniques when they know their child will face or is facing a distressing situation. For adolescents with anorexia, the most distressing situations usually involve food and eating either pre, post, or during the actual mealtime. Therefore, the distraction strategy you decide upon should coincide with the time you feel your adolescent's anxiety will be at its peak.

- **Following a meal** – anorexia can make your adolescent feel extremely guilty after a meal as they may be flooded with self-loathing thoughts and thoughts of failure due to loss of control. It is usually when your adolescent is in this state that they are tempted to purge the calories they have consumed either by vomiting and/or exercising. After meals is a good time to introduce activities that distract them from these thoughts.

- **Prior to a meal** – many adolescents become very agitated prior to eating as they are consumed with anticipatory anxiety just thinking about the quantity and foods their parents will make them eat. They may feel they need to know exactly what their parents are cooking, and what ingredients they are putting in the meal. It is easier to keep your child out of the kitchen and probably a good time to use soothing techniques and/or distraction techniques.

- **During the meal** – eating the meal can also be a difficult time so this is when you would use distraction. Many families sit together during meals and try and initiate conversations about daily events unrelated to food that will distract their adolescent. Many parents allow their adolescent to watch their favorite TV shows, YouTube videos, or play games whilst eating as a distraction. Sometimes your adolescent can become obsessive about the calories in the meal and will immediately start counting calories without any ability to stop. If this is the case, help your adolescent drown out the obsessive calorie counting thoughts. A good method is by getting your adolescent to put headphones on with distracting songs, audiobooks, etc. It is difficult to count calories and listen to something else.

It is up to you to know your enemy—the anorexia. You need to know when the anorexia is at its strongest. Is it the morning meal or evening meal? When the anorexia is at its strongest be more prepared with strategies and a plan to manage your adolescent's distress.

Your adolescent's distress is not just restricted to food, eating, and weight gain as there will be occasions throughout the treatment when your child will become distressed in response to thoughts about their body image especially when clothes become tighter and/or they see their reflection in the mirror. Perhaps it may be when they need to eat in front of others or return to school. Learn to read those situations quickly before your child climbs too high on their emotional wave. Remember the lower on the wave they are, the easier it is to get them back down and self-regulate.

Parents usually know their adolescent's likes and dislikes so any distraction strategy you use will usually be more successful if it is centered around your adolescent's interests.

Following are only a few strategies that many parents have found useful. You can be creative and come up with your own as no one knows your child better than you. Remember the strategy needs to help your adolescent fully focus their attention on the activity you present. The activity needs to be a "thought blocker" and the best way to block thought is to enjoy the activity. Early on in treatment, the strategy cannot involve a large expenditure of energy; therefore, strategies need to be sedentary. As your adolescent gains more weight, activities can be more active like going for a short walk, etc. However, you need to be guided by your therapist regarding any additional exercise.

## Distraction strategies

- **Zentangle** is an intricate art form that requires a lot of concentration, and many artistic adolescents usually love this technique. It is normally called "yoga for the mind."
- **Colouring in books** are usually very relaxing and mind-consuming.
- **TV and YouTube** are great distractions especially 'Funniest Home Videos' and 'Funniest Cat/Animal Videos.' Cat videos are actually the most-watched YouTube videos and very funny and distractive.
- **Creative Arts** if your child is creative and loves making things, then be creative with them.
- **Audiobooks** if your child was an avid reader, listening to one of their favorite novels whilst eating can take their mind off the meal.
- **Online Free Jig-Saw Puzzles,** games, etc.

## Self-soothing strategies

- Breathing techniques. Breath techniques are very grounding. A quick and simple exercise is triangle breathing. Picture a triangle and breathe up the triangle in for 3, hold down the triangle for 3, and breathe slowly out following the base of the triangle for 6. It is important that the breath out is always longer than the breath in.
- Guided meditations and visualization – there are many apps, or you can guide your child.
- Music is always a good distraction for adolescents and has an excellent track record for reducing stress and anxiety. Help your adolescent make lists of music that correspond to their mood. Uplifting songs, calming songs, and powerful songs during meals can distract and encourage them to battle their anorexia. Slower music, particularly classical music is definitely soothing to both heart and mind.
- Humming is one of the simplest techniques to self-soothe and shown to reduce stress, induce calmness, lower blood pressure, enhance sleep, and produce neurochemicals such as oxytocin. It's worth a try!

## UTILIZING THE "SPACE BETWEEN" MEALS TO CONNECT WITH YOUR CHILD

Without a doubt, mealtimes are usually the most distressing and conflictual times when dealing with an adolescent with anorexia leaving parents totally exhausted. Also during mealtimes, an adolescent can feel that parents have become the enemy and that they don't understand them. Their parents, who used to be a source of comfort, have now become their source of distress. However, good parenting is making the tough "NO" decisions regarding what is best for your adolescent. Allowing them not to eat sufficiently is one of those "NO" difficult decisions despite knowing that you may be upsetting them.

Some parents can feel relief when their adolescent goes to their room and wants to be alone. This is ok for short periods, but it's important to realize that your adolescent is in their room dealing with the distress alone and probably the perfect time for anorexia to increase the guilt connected to eating as well as self-hatred for having eaten.

The "space between" is a valuable opportunity to show your adolescent that you are not angry with them, understand them, want to support them, and want to connect with them by doing some enjoyable activity and/or spending time together. It can be anything as simple as going for a drive together, sitting by the beach, watching a movie, or even reading together. The activity is not important, it is the act of reconnecting with your adolescent and showing them you are still their source of comfort and that they do not have to deal with the anorexia and horrible thoughts and internal dialogue alone. Human beings are social creatures and connection is a biological imperative activated by our attachment drive. There is always a deep longing to belong, to be accepted, and receive comfort from others. When managing your adolescence always remember to try and **reduce the fear and increase feelings of safety and connection**. Sometimes just holding your adolescent's hand can be a great source of comfort. Your therapist will provide you and your adolescent with many more strategies to reduce your adolescent's distress and help them manage the countless AN symptoms and distorted thinking.

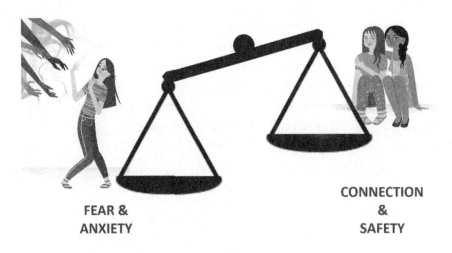

**FEAR & ANXIETY**

**CONNECTION & SAFETY**

# SIMPLE TIPS TO HELP YOUR CHILD MANAGE THEIR ANXIETY

Current research shows that there is a major association between anxiety and eating disorders. A high percentage of adolescents with anorexia suffer from childhood anxiety that is predictive of more severe ED symptoms.[36] It is expected that adolescents with premorbid anxiety will continue to be highly anxious following weight restoration. During anorexia, your adolescent will develop many unrealistic fears and thoughts about food that will exacerbate any pre-existing anxiety. Your adolescent will also be affected with 'anticipatory anxiety,' which means they will become very anxious thinking about confronting the next meal you are preparing even before you have presented the meal.

Put simply, anxiety is a result of thoughts convincing you that you will not cope with a certain situation or event. Example: ***Thought*** – I will not do any good on my exam. You keep worrying and ruminating on that thought continually until you convince yourself that you will fail despite all your efforts to study for the exam. You actually build a mental picture of yourself failing. By constantly thinking about the negative thought/outcome you continually **"reinforce"** it, and by reinforcing it you strengthen a negative neural pathway.

A good way to manage this anxiety is to replace the negative picture/thought with positive affirmations and creating a positive picture of getting an "A" for the exam. You need to repeat the positive affirmations, and thoughts and visualize your success as often as you can throughout the day when you are calm. You will eventually convince your brain that you will get an "A." You are actually reprogramming your brain by creating new pathways and getting rid of the negative (anxiety) pathways and reducing anxiety.

# THE NECESSITY OF EXPOSURE

An adolescent with anorexia and high levels of anxiety will usually develop thoughts and fears about certain foods that they have classed as "bad" together with the worrying consequences these foods will have on their body. The adolescent may also develop anxiety about eating in front of others or going out to eat in public. Their constant worrying about these issues will only reinforce the beliefs. Despite your adolescent's anxiety you will need to help your child confront these fears by exposing them to what they fear. This is called **exposure therapy**. Therefore, you will need to gently get your adolescent to eat the feared foods and eat in public and with others. If you do not expose your adolescent to what makes them anxious, full recovery will be difficult to achieve.

Many of these situations will induce anticipatory anxiety. A good way to help your child manage these situations and their anxiety is to teach your child deep breathing exercises. A good strategy is to develop "check-in" points throughout the day. This is done by asking your child to sit comfortably, place their hands on their tummy, close their eyes, and take slow deep breaths to the bottom of their stomach and feel the rise and fall of their tummy as they concentrate on their breathing. You also ask them to visualize themselves being calm and present. They will need to do this for two minutes 10–12 times per day. Check-ins can also be helpful pre and post meals. This exercise can be done together, or you can guide your child through the exercise. The constant repetition of check-ins aims to teach your child to self-regulate. Many parents also find the exercise useful in reducing their own stress and anxiety regarding refeeding. Your therapist will also be able to treat your adolescent's anxiety whilst you concentrate on renourishing your adolescent.

# FINAL WORDS

## What does recovery look like?

### *Full recovery – the ideal*

- Return to "normalized" eating. This means being able to eat spontaneously when hungry and independently.
- Ability to eat a wide variety of foods without fear of calories and/or weight gain.
- Freedom from anorexic thoughts and preoccupations with food and weight.
- Loving and accepting one's body the way it is despite some "normative discontent," which many people may experience but which does not impact on lifestyle.
- A return to normal physical growth and development that allows the adolescent to achieve their growth potential. For females, this will include a return of menses.
- Participating in normal adolescent activities such as school, socializing with friends and family, engaging in sport, and activities of interest.

Whilst weight restoration may be achieved rapidly, it may take some time for your child to reach full physical and psychological recovery as described above. All adolescents vary in their stage of recovery, and much is dependent on their personality traits, length of illness, and pre-existing mental health issues. The importance of receiving individual psychological support for your adolescent cannot be underestimated. It is also important for parents to receive as much support as needed in order to sustain the treatment and continue to support their adolescent. Anorexia is an insidious illness because the sufferer, in many instances, does not believe they are unwell and therefore, is resistant to accept help. This rejection of support takes its toll on everyone involved, especially parents. However, full recovery is possible; therefore, I encourage you to believe in your parental abilities and your determination fueled by your love for your child.

# APPENDIX

## Meal and snack plan samples

The following plans provide an example of the quantity of food your child needs to eat for main meals and also what constitutes high-calorie snacks. The meal and snack plan is ONLY a guide to help you understand intake requirements for weight restoration and should be used as a guide. Feel free to interchange foods of similar calorie content. Your child may prefer to remain on a meal plan; however, it is not a good idea to stick rigorously to the same meal plan every day as it only reinforces rigidity. The goal is for your child to return to normalized eating, which means eating whatever is available and/or served by parents without fear. Research suggests that consumption of a varied diet can be related to improved outcomes in anorexia nervosa.[37]

*Sample of appropriate snacks to give your child*

*(Courtesy of Ingrid Hilton, Dietician)*

|  | Morning Tea | Afternoon Tea | Supper |
|---|---|---|---|
| **Monday** | 2 x Anzac biscuits + apple, 250 ml full cream milk or soy milk | 1 cup fruit, 200 g yogurt, ½ cup toasted granola | 350 ml milk with 2 tbs Milo + piece of fruit |
| **Tuesday** | Go natural' muesli bar, 250 ml full cream milk or soy milk | Slice grain toast with tsp butter and banana sliced on top, 1 cup milk | 300 ml milk with 2 tbs milo + 2 Anzac biscuits |
| **Wednesday** | Muesli bar + piece of fruit, 250 ml full cream milk or soy milk | Fruit Smoothie (1 banana, 300 ml milk, 150 g yogurt full cream, 1 tsp honey, 2 heaped tablespoons oat bran, 2 dates) | Chai powder sachet with 350 ml milk, tsp honey + fruit |
| **Thursday** | Sesame snap bar (40 g) + piece of fruit, 250 ml full cream milk or soy milk | 2 x soy and linseed Vita Wheat lunch slice, 2 x 21 g cheese + avocado | 'Sustagen' tetra pack + piece of fruit |

| | | | |
|---|---|---|---|
| **Friday** | Cheese/herb scone with tsp butter, 250 ml milk | 1 x bounce ball + piece of fruit, 250 ml full cream milk or soy milk | Hot chocolate 350 ml with biscuit |
| **Saturday** | 1 x fruit/nut bread + butter, 250 ml full cream milk or soy milk | 1 x 'Emma/Toms' juice, 4 Vita Wheat biscuits with 2 tbs nut spread | Sustagen' tetra pack + piece of fruit |
| **Sunday** | 1 x dark chocolate and berry muffin, 250 ml full cream milk or soy milk | Fruit smoothie (1 banana, 300 ml milk, 150 g yogurt full cream, 1 tsp honey, 2 heaped tablespoons oat bran, 2 dates) | 350 ml milk + 2 tbs Milo + piece of fruit |

## Sample of a meal plan

*(Courtesy of Ingrid Hilton, Dietician)*

| | Breakfast | Lunch | Dinner | Dessert |
|---|---|---|---|---|
| **Day one** | Bowl porridge made with full cream milk/ soy (250 ml), 1 banana, 100 g yogurt, 2 tbs LSA, 1 tsp honey or brown sugar | Chicken/ avocado/ cheese Sandwich (grain bread), 1 glass of juice | Spinach and ricotta cannelloni with parmesan cheese, slice of ciabatta with butter, salad, orange juice | 2 scoops of ice cream |
| **Day two** | 2 x slices grain bread, 2 x tsp butter, 1 tsp vegemite + 1 tsp jam or honey, piece of fruit, yogurt | Vegetarian frittata (potato, egg, cheese, milk etc.), salad, glass of juice | Chicken and vegetable stir fry with cashews (oyster sauce or teriyaki) with steamed rice, glass of juice | 1 cup yogurt full cream flavored + fruit |
| **Day three** | 1 x Bircher muesli (soaked in 1 x glass fruit juice & yogurt), 250 ml milk, 1 banana or mango, 1 tsp honey + slithered almonds | Chicken pesto pasta salad with fetta, 1 x milk, 1 x piece of fruit | Lamb/mushroom casserole with mashed sweet potato (made with milk/butter), steamed vegetables, wholemeal dinner roll with butter, glass of juice | Freddo frog + Glass of milk |

|  | Breakfast | Lunch | Dinner | Dessert |
|---|---|---|---|---|
| Day four | 2 x wholegrain toast, 2 x butter, 2 x eggs, ½ avocado, 1 glass of milk | Cheese, ham, avocado, and tomato toasted sandwich (with butter), 1 x juice | Pan-fried salmon or fish, potato/sweet potato wedges, salad with dressing, slice of bread with butter, glass of juice | 1 cup full cream custard + piece of fruit |
| Day five | 2 x Special K (high fiber), 1 banana, 250 ml full cream cows or soy milk | Smoked salmon, avocado, cream cheese and salad sandwich, yogurt, piece of fruit | Roasted vegetable and feta quiche with salad (dressing), 1 dinner roll with butter, glass of juice | 1 cup Calciyum |
| Day six | 2 x wholegrain bread, 2 x butter, 1 x nut butter, 1 x jam or honey, piece of fruit, yogurt | 3 x hand sushi rolls with avocado/ salmon, glass of milk, piece of fruit | Pasta Bolognaise with parmesan cheese + side salad, 1 slice garlic bread, glass of juice | 2 scoops of ice cream |
| Day seven | 2 x Weetbix (wholegrain), banana, 250 ml full cream milk cows or soy | Cheese, egg, and vegetable quiche with salad, glass of fruit juice | Roast chicken with gravy, roast potatoes, pumpkin, steamed beans, and peas, glass of juice | Slice of cheese-cake |
| Day eight | 2 x wholemeal toast, 2 x butter, 1 small tin baked beans, glass orange juice or large piece of fruit | Chicken, egg, cashew nuts and rice salad, 1 yogurt, 1 cup of juice | Beef Rendang (coconut curry) with rice or rice noodles, 3 papadams + yogurt sauce, glass of juice | Cup yogurt full cream with ¼ cup almonds |

# REFERENCES

1. Lock J & LeGrange D., *Treatment Manual for Anorexia Nervosa – A Family Based Approach*, Second Ed. 2013, Guilford Press, NY, London.

2. Hoek, H. W. (2006). Incidence, prevalence and mortality of anorexia nervosa and other eating disorders. *Current Opinion in Psychiatry*, 19 (4), 389-394.

3. The National Eating Disorders Collaboration. (2012a). An Integrated Response to Complexity – National Eating Disorders Framework 2012. Sydney: NEDC.

4. Blinder, B.J. (2001). Anorexia in Males **http://www.ltspeed.com/ bjblinder/anmales.htm.**

5. Arcelus, J. M., Mitchell, A., Wales, J., Nielsen, S. (2011). Mortality rates in patients with anorexia nervosa and other eating disorders: A meta-analysis of 36 studies. *Archives General Psychiatry 68*(7), 724-731.

6. Franko, D. L, Keshaviah, A., Eddy, K., Krishna, M., Davis, M. C., Keel, P. K. Herzog, D. B. (2013). Do Mortality Rates in Eating Disorders Change Over Time? A Longitudinal Look at Anorexia Nervosa and Bulimia Nervosa. *American Journal of Psychiatry*, 170 (8), 917-925.

7. American Psychiatric Association. (2013). *Diagnostic and statistical manual of mental disorders – 5th edition.* American Psychiatric Association: Washington, DC.

8. Damiano, S., Reece, J., Atkins, L., and Reid, S. (2015). Maladaptive Schemas in Adolescent Females with Anorexia Nervosa and Implications for Treatment. *Eating Behaviors: The Journal of Prevention and Treatment*, 16, 64-71.

9. Damiano, S., Reece, J., Reid, S., Atkins, L., and Patton, G. (2015). Empirically Derived Typologies of Adolescent Females with Anorexia Nervosa: Understanding General Psychopathology and Treatment Implications. *Eating Behaviors: Journal of Prevention and Treatment*, 23, 223-241.

10. Whitelaw, M. Lee, K, J., Gilbertson, H. and Sawyer, S. (2018). Predictors of Complications in Anorexia Nervosa and Atypical Anorexia Nervosa: Degree of Underweight or Extent and Recency of Weight Loss? *Journal of Adolescent Health*, 63 (6), 663-804.

11. Favaro, A. and Santonastaso, P. (2016). Anticipation of age at onset in anorexia nervosa. *European Psychiatry*, 33, 6.

12. Klump, K. (2013). Puberty as a critical risk period for eating disorders: A review of human and animal studies. *Hormone Behaviour*, 64 (2), 399-410.

13. The National Eating Disorders Collaboration. (2012a). *An Integrated Response to Complexity – National Eating Disorders Framework 2012*. NEDC: Sydney, Australia.

14. Wade, T. D. (2010). Genetic influences on eating disorders. In Agras, W. S. (Ed.), *Oxford Handbook of Eating Disorders*. Oxford University Press: New York, USA.

15. Baker, J. H., and Munn-Chernoff, M. A. (2014). Genetic Vulnerability to Eating and Substance use Disorders. In Timothy D. Brewerton and Amy Baker Dennis (Eds.), *Eating Disorders, Addictions and Substance Use Disorders: Research, Clinical and Treatment Perspectives*. Springer: Berlin.

16. Kaye, W. H., Bulik, C. M., Thornton, L., Barbarich, N., Masters, K., Price Foundation Collaborative Group. (2004). Comorbidity of anxiety disorders with anorexia and bulimia nervosa. *American Journal of Psychiatry*. 161 (12), 2215-2221.

17. Anderluh, M. B., Tchanturia, K., Rabe – Hesketh, S. and Treasure, J. (2003). Childhood obsessive-compulsive personality traits in adult women with eating disorders: Defining a broader eating disorder phenotype. *The American Journal of Psychitry*, 160 (2), 242-247.

18. Bulik, C. M., Tozzi, F., Anderson, C., Mazzeo, S. E., Aggen, S. and Sullivan, P. F. (2003). The relation between eating disorders and components of perfectionism. *American Journal of Psychiatry*, 160 (2), 366-368.

19. Fassino, S., Abbate-Daga, G., Amianto, F., Leombruni, P., Boggio, S. and Rovera, G. G. (2002). Temperament and character profile of eating

disorders: a controlled study with the Temperament and Character Inventory. *International Journal of Eating Disorders*, 32(4), 412-425.

20. The National Eating Disorders Collaboration (2010a). *Eating Disorders Prevention, Treatment and Management: An Evidence Review*. NEDC: Sydney, Australia.

21. Sundgot-Borgen, J. and Tortveit, M. K. (2004). Prevalence of eating disorders in elite athletes is higher than in the general population. *Clinical Journal of Sport Medicine*, 14 (1), 25-32.

22. Avdagić, S., Barić, I., Keser, I., Cecić I., Šatalić, Z., Bobić, J., Gomzi, M. (2009). Differences in peak bone density between male and female students. *Archives of Industrial Hygiene and Toxicology*. 60 (1), 79-86.

23. Kan, C., Cardi, V., Stahl, D., Treasure, J. (2019) Editorial. Precision Psychiatry – What it means for eating disorders? *Eur Eat Disorders Rev.* 27:3-7.

24. Lock J, (2015): An Update on Evidence-Based Psychosocial Treatments for Eating Disorders in Children and Adolescents, *Journal of Clinical Child & Adolescent Psychology*, DOI: 10.1080/15374416.2014.971458.

25. Lask B, & Frampton I, *Eating Disorders & the Brain*, 2011, Pub Wiley-Blackwell.

26. Nunn K, Hanstock T, & Lask B, *The Who's Who of the Brain*, 2008, Jessica Kingsley Pub. London & Philadelphia.

27. Nunn K, Frampton I, Gordon I, Lask B, 2008: The Fault is not in her parents but in her insula – a neurobiological hypothesis of anorexia. E*ur Eat Disord Rev*, 16(5):355-60.

28. Heruc, A. H., Little, T. J., Kohen, M., Madden, S., Clarke, S., Horowitz, M. and Feinle-Bisset, C. (2018). Appetite perceptions, gastrointestinal symptoms, ghrelin, peptide YY and state anxiety are disturbed in adolescent females with anorexia nervosa and only partially restored with short-term refeeding. *Nutrients*, 11, (59).

29. Waldholtz, M. and Andersen, B. (1990). Gastrointestinal symptoms in anorexia nervosa, a prospective study. *Gastroenterology*, 98 (6), 1415-1419.

30. Kleiman S, Carroll I, Tarantino L, Bulik C, 2015: Gut Feelings: A role for the intestinal microbiota in anorexia nervosa? *Int J Eating Disorders*, 48:449-451.

31. Singer T, and Klimeck OM, (2014 ) Empathy and Compassion. *Current Biology*, Vol 24, No.18, R876.

32. Figures provided by https://peacepathway.org/.

33. Kinnaird E, Oakley M, Lawrence V, Shergill S, & Tchanturia K. (2021) *Journal of Eating Disorders*. 9:42 https://doi.org/10.1186/s40337-021-00397-6.

34. Lie SO, Bulik CM, Andreassen OA, Ro O, & Bang L (2021) The association between bullying and eating disorders: A case-control study. *International Jr of Eating Disorders*, 1-10: DOI:10.1002/eat.23522.

35. Zucker N, 2008, Off the Cuff - A Parent Skills Book for the Management of Disordered Eating. Duke University Medical Centre.

36. Kaye W, Wierenga CE, Bailer UF, Simmons AN, Bischoff-Grethe A. 2013, Nothing Tastes as Good as Skinny Feels: The Neurobiology of Anorexia Nervosa. *Trends in Neuroscience*, 36(2).

37. Schebendach JE, Mayer LE, Devlin MJ, Attia E, Contento IR, Wolf RL, Walsh T., 2011, Food choice and diet variety in weight-restored patients with anorexia nervosa. *J Am Diet Assoc*. 111:732-736.

Printed in Great Britain
by Amazon

39526495R00056